MEDIA MANUALS

Your Film & the Lab

MEDIA MANUALS

TV CAMERA OPERATION
Gerald Millerson

BASIC TV STAGING
Gerald Millerson

THE USE OF MICROPHONES
Alec Nisbett

YOUR FILM & THE LAB
L. Bernard Happé

TV LIGHTING METHODS
Gerald Millerson

TV SOUND OPERATIONS
E. G. M. Alkin

Forthcoming titles

16 mm Film Cutting

Timing for Animation

Using Videotape

The Small TV Studio

The Motion Picture Camera

TV Graphics and Titling

The Animation Rostrum

The Practice of TV Production

Your Film & the Lab

L. Bernard Happé

A Focal Press Book

Communication Arts Books

HASTINGS HOUSE, PUBLISHERS

New York, NY 10016

ISBN 0 8038 8596 2 (Cloth Edition)
ISBN 0 8038 8595 4 (Text Edition)

Library of Congress Catalog Card Number : 74–1409

Printed by Johnson Riddle & Co. Ltd, and bound by the Pitman Press.

Contents

TR
886.2
.H36
1974

THE POSITION OF THE LABORATORY	8	STEP PRINTERS	48
Front-end operations		Control of printing light Colour	
Release printing		Uses	
RUSH PRINT SERVICES	10	OPTICAL PRINTERS	50
Rush print viewing		Light sources	
PREPARATORY WORK &	12	Special effects	
ANSWER PRINTING		CONTINUOUS OPTICAL PRINTERS	52
First married print		Multiple printing	
RELEASE PRINT MANUFACTURE	14	POSITIVE PROCESSING	54
Despatch preparation		EQUIPMENT	
TYPES OF FILM	16	Sound track striping	
Camera original materials		GENERAL FILM HANDLING	56
Print materials		EQUIPMENT 1	
FILM GAUGES	18	Measuring equipment	
Perforations		Synchronisers	
FILM MANUFACTURE &	20	GENERAL FILM HANDLING	58
IDENTIFICATION		EQUIPMENT 2	
Perforation and winding details		Width of splices	
STOCK EDGE NUMBERS	22	NEGATIVE IDENTIFICATION &	60
Identifying the position of a frame		PACKING	
IMAGE FORMATS	24	Care of film	
Wide gauge film		PROTECTION IN TRANSIT	62
A WIND & B WIND	26	Air freight	
EMULSION POSITIONS		CAMERA REPORTS	64
Projection		Film Producers Association report	
THE B & W NEGATIVE & POSITIVE	28	form	
PROCESS		Other report forms	
Print making		CAMERA REPORT DETAILS	66
THE B & W REVERSAL PROCESS	30	Essential details	
Reversal exposure		Other information	
Copying reversal images		NEGATIVE BREAK-DOWN &	68
THE COLOUR NEGATIVE &	32	MAKE-UP	
POSITIVE PROCESS		Make-up into rolls	
Colour negatives		RUSH PRINT GRADING (1)	70
Colour prints		Black-and-white rushes	
THE COLOUR REVERSAL	34	Colour rushes	
PROCESS		RUSH PRINT GRADING (2)	72
Camera reversal films		One-light printing	
PROCESSING MACHINES	36	RUSH PRINTING RECORDS	74
Sprocketless processors		Additive printers	
NEGATIVE PROCESSING	38	Subtractive printers	
EQUIPMENT		EXPOSURE RATING	76
Higher speed processing		Acceptable exposure variations	
REVERSAL PROCESSING	40	Effects of exposure on image	
EQUIPMENT		quality	
Colour reversal processing		RUSH PRINT REPORTS	78
PRINTING MACHINES	42	Abbreviations	
CONTACT PRINTERS	44	RUSH PRINT DELIVERY REPORTS	80
Sound track printing		Negative defects	
PRINTER LIGHT CONTROL	46		
Exposure steps			

NEGATIVE MOVEMENT RECORDS **82**
& REPRINTS
  Reprints

NEGATIVE STORAGE RECORDS **84**
  Storage by customers

SIMPLIFIED RECORD SYSTEMS **86**
  Returning film to the
    production company

OPTICALS: TRANSITION EFFECTS **88**
  Fades
  Dissolves
  Wipes

OPTICALS: OTHER SPECIAL **90**
EFFECTS

OPTICALS: IMAGE COMBINATION **92**
  Split screen shots
  Adding background to studio shots

MARKINGS FOR OPTICAL EFFECTS **94**
  Fades
  Dissolves
  Wipes
  Hold and freeze frames
  Other effects

SPECIFICATIONS FOR OPTICAL **96**
WORK
  Examples

OPTICAL SPECIFICATION **98**
SHEETS (1)
  First example
  Second example

OPTICAL SPECIFICATION **100**
SHEETS (2)
  Additional reminders

OPTICAL SPECIFICATION **102**
SHEETS (3)
  A & B Printing

METHODS OF DUPE PRINTING **104**
  Black-and-white negative
  Colour negative
  Colour reversal intermediate
  Dupes from reversal materials

PRINTING OPTICALS: MASTERS **106**
& DUPES
  Fade-out
  Fade-in
  Dissolve
  Optical printers

PRINTING OPTICALS: CRIs **108**
  Fades

PRINTING OPTICALS: WIPES **110**
  Straight horizontal wipe

PRINTING OPTICALS: **112**
SUPERIMPOSED TITLES
  Reversal originals

PRINTING OPTICALS: COLOUR **114**
LETTER TITLES
  Making mattes

TITLE AREAS **116**
  35mm wide-screen prints
  Anamorphic 35mm
  35mm film for Television use
  16mm film

PHOTOGRAPHIC SOUND TRACK **118**
TRANSFER
  Work of the sound department
  Making photographic sound
    tracks

PHOTOGRAPHIC SOUND **120**
CAMERA LOGS
  A record of what you want

PHOTOGRAPHIC SOUND **122**
PROCESSING
  Density testing

PHOTOGRAPHIC SOUND **124**
PRINTING
  Cross-modulation tests

NEGATIVE CUTTING: WORK **126**
PRINTS

PICTURE AND TRACK **128**
SYNCHRONISATION
  The sync-plop
  Picture and Sound preparation

WORK PRINTS: REEL MAKE-UP **130**
  Printing lengths

LEADERS (1) **132**
  Leader patterns

LEADERS (2) **134**
  SMPTE Leader
  EBU Leader

CUE MARKS **136**
  Form of cue marks

NEGATIVE SELECTION FOR **138**
CUTTING
  The cutting log

CUTTING PICTURE & TRACK **140**
NEGATIVES
  Adding printer cues

A & B CUTTING **142**
First example
Second example

CHECKER-BOARD CUTTING **144**
Splices

ZERO CUT & AUTO-OPTICALS **146**
Auto-opticals

LIMITATIONS OF A & B CUTTING **148**
Length of effects
Length of scenes
Proximity of effects

NEGATIVE CLEANING **150**
Cleaning methods

PROTECTIVE FACILITIES **152**
Black-and-white
Colour

GRADING FOR THE ANSWER **154**
PRINT (1)
Communication with the grader
Applying corrections

GRADING FOR THE ANSWER **156**
PRINT (2)
Electronic analysers
Photographic tests

ANSWER PRINT STAGES **158**
Liaison with the production team

ANSWER PRINT PRESENTATION **160**
Viewing conditions—35mm
Viewing conditions—16mm

TRAILERS & POST-PRODUCTION **162**
WORK
Preparing material for trailers
Other post-production work

CHANGES OF FORMAT **164**
Reduction and enlargement
Alterations of frame format
Printers

ENLARGEMENT PRINTING: **166**
16MM TO 35MM
Super-16

ENLARGEMENT PRINTING: **168**
35MM TO 70MM
Anamorphic negatives
Flat negatives
16mm originals

UNSQUEEZE PRINTING **170**
Prints for television from
anamorphic negatives

REDUCTION PRINTING: **172**
35MM TO 16MM
Printing methods

REDUCTION PRINTING TO 8MM **174**
& SUPER-8
Multi-rank intermediates

MAGNETIC SOUND **176**
Specification of magnetic stripes
Sound synchronization

RELEASE PRINTING FROM 35MM **178**
NEGATIVE
Making 16mm prints

RELEASE PRINTING FROM 16MM **180**
REVERSAL
Making 35mm prints

RELEASE PRINTING FROM 16MM **182**
NEGATIVE
16mm prints
35mm prints

RELEASE PRINT METHODS **184**
Splices in release prints

POSITIVE ASSEMBLY WORK **186**
After-treatment of prints

PROCESSING FILM FOR **188**
TELEVISION
Black-and-white prints
Colour prints

VIEWING PRINTS FOR **190**
TELEVISION USE
Viewing conditions

THE USE OF FILM ON TELEVISION **192**
News and real life documentary
Full length drama
Film inserts
Advertising spots and commercials

LABORATORY CHARGES & **194**
BUDGETING (1)
General principles

LABORATORY CHARGES & **196**
BUDGETING (2)
Outline Budget
Fundamental components

LABORATORY CHARGES & **198**
BUDGETING (3)
Special effects
Release prints
Television commercials

TERMS OF BUSINESS **200**
Rectifying faults

IN CONCLUSION
FURTHER READING } **202**

GLOSSARY **203**

The Position of the Laboratory

The motion picture laboratory exists to provide a range of technical services which complement the work of production in the studio and on location. They also produce the release prints which are eventually distributed for public presentation. The organisation and operations of the laboratory are therefore generally divided into two main areas: 'front-end' work for the production organisation carried out on an individually specialised basis in closest co-operation with the creative workers at the studio, while 'release print' work involves the application of bulk manufacture methods and quality control.

Front-end operations

The front-end operations for the production organisation may themselves be divided into two main groups which can be described as rush print processing and answer printing. The first covers all work between the receipt of the exposed negative from the camera and the delivery of the resultant daily rush prints to the editors' cutting room for synchronisation with the sound record and viewing by the production team.

The second stage covers the preparation of the answer print, which is the first completely finished copy of the film submitted for the approval of the producer. This work can include co-operation with the special effects department of the studio, the preparation of optical effects required by the editor for continuity purposes and the processing and rush printing of the photographic sound track negative transferred from the finally mixed magnetic recordings.

It also includes the cutting and assembly of the various scenes of picture negative to match the work print supplied by the editor and the printing of picture and sound as a combined married copy. At this stage the operation of grading or timing each scene of the picture must be carried out to ensure that the colour and density is consistent throughout and that the dramatic continuity of lighting mood required by the cameraman and director is realised.

Release printing

After answer print approval the laboratory will be concerned with the manufacture of further copies (i.e. release printing). The requirements may range from the two or three prints needed for television transmission to the scores required for the release of a film in general cinema theatre distribution, and the many hundreds of copies sometimes needed from TV advertising 'commercials'. Depending on the type of order, release print operations may therefore include the preparation of duplicate negatives for safety in repeated use or for change of format when narrow-gauge prints in 16mm or 8mm are to be used. Release print orders are generally placed by the distribution company rather than the production organisation.

PRODUCTION

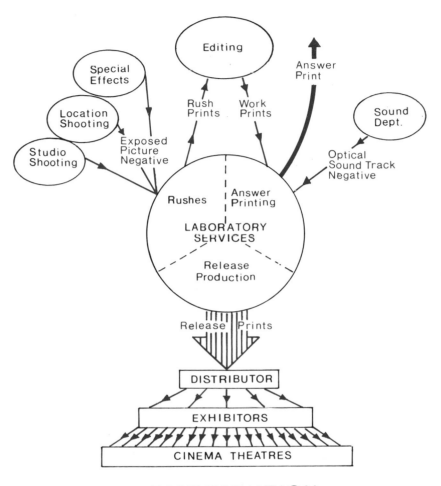

DISTRIBUTION

THE POSITION OF THE LABORATORY The Laboratory provides the
technical services which link all phases of film production and the resultant
release prints to be shown in the cinema.

Rush Print Services

Exposed picture negative from the production camera crews working at the studio, or on location, will normally be sent to the laboratory each evening. It will be sent with clear instructions for the processing and printing required, as picture negative reports or camera logs prepared by a camera assistant for the director and cameraman.

At the laboratory, after developing the film is inspected and in accordance with the camera log subdivided into those scenes and takes which are required to be printed and those which are not (negative breakdown). The sections for printing are joined together into rolls which become the laboratory's processing unit, identified by the production title and a laboratory serial number. Detailed records are prepared on the basis of the camera log information. The negative not specified for printing, referred to as second negative, will be set aside for storage as 'hold takes', and 'NG takes'.

After make up the selected scenes are examined by a grading operator to determine how this new material shall be printed for the first time, taking into consideration any special instructions given by the cameraman or director in the report sheet.

When the characteristics of each scene have been decided and recorded, a positive print is made from the assembled roll and processed through a developing machine, either colour or black-and-white. Immediate priority is always given in the laboratory to this type of work and these prints are known as daily rush prints, usually abbreviated to 'dailies' or 'rushes'.

Rush print viewing

Each rush print is projected immediately after processing and viewed by a skilled operator who prepares a detailed report on what he sees for the editor or cameraman. This is often done by the laboratory contact man, who is responsible for liaison between the production company and the laboratory operators. After viewing, the rush prints and the reports are delivered to or collected by the cutting room staff of the production editor, with copies of all reports for the cameraman concerned.

The rolls of negative are usually kept readily available for a few days, in case the editor should require reprints, and are then returned for storage with the necessary identification records. A laboratory will normally offer an over-night service for negative developing and rush printing: exposed material reaching the laboratory during the late evening is processed soon after midnight and break-down, grading, printing and developing follow for viewing in the early morning. Rush prints and reports are therefore available for the cutting room staff to start work on the morning of the day after photography.

10

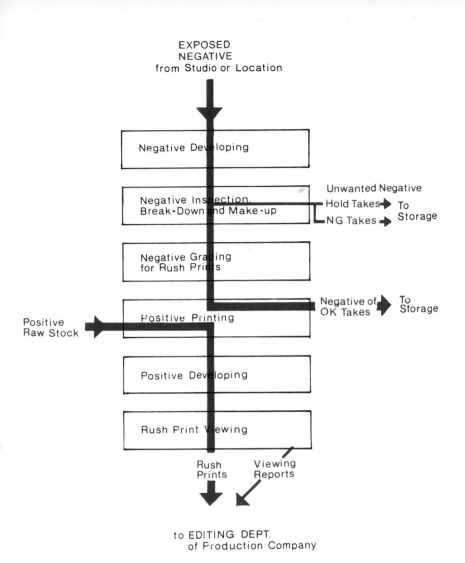

EXPOSED
NEGATIVE
from Studio or Location

Negative Developing

Negative Inspection,
Break-Down and Make-up

Unwanted Negative
Hold Takes → To
NG Takes → Storage

Negative Grading
for Rush Prints

Positive Printing

Negative of → To
OK Takes → Storage

Positive
Raw Stock

Positive Developing

Rush Print Viewing

Rush   Viewing
Prints   Reports

to EDITING DEPT.
of Production Company

RUSH PRINT SERVICES   As the first step. the Laboratory develops, inspects and identifies the photographed film and returns the resultant prints of each day's work for editing.

Preparatory Work & Answer Printing

During preparatory work instructions come primarily from the editor: as the work of editing goes forward, photographic effects not appearing in the original negative may be found necessary. Some of these will be trick shots requiring the studio special effects department or a specialist title organisation but many transitional effects, such as fades and dissolves, and optical effects, such as changes of image size or position, will be done by the laboratory to the editor's specification.

During editing the sound records will be assembled and combined into a master magnetic sound track by mixing together all the separate components of dialogue, music and sound effects. When finally approved this is transferred to a photographic sound track negative and sent to the laboratory for developing and rush printing.

The editor can now pass the final work prints of both sound and picture to the laboratory for cutting and answer printing. The laboratory identifies all the scenes and takes finally included and locates them in storage. The selected negative scenes then pass to the negative cutter, and each is cut to match the corresponding section of the work print and spliced into the correct sequence. Identification and protective leaders are added at the beginning and end. The unused portions of the selected scenes, known as 'trims' are identified and stored. A continuity record of each assembled reel, giving the scene and take number, its length and description is prepared for subsequent printing operations.

When the picture negative is ready the printing data for each scene and take must be obtained, either from the rush printing information or by a new grading assessment. Any detailed comments on the colour balance and density of the rush prints by the director and cameraman must be taken into consideration.

First married print
A first married print from the cut negative will then be made on this initial grading information and viewed with the cameraman and editor for comments and advice on the character of colour reproduction required, as well as sound quality and synchronisation. Any necessary grading corrections are then applied to each scene and a further corrected print prepared. This sequence of operations may have to be repeated, until the grader, the laboratory contact man and the editor or other production company representative agree that a consistent copy embodying the dramatic character required by the director has been obtained. It is then submitted by the laboratory for approval as the answer print. When approved, the scene-to-scene grading is recorded as final, to be used in making all further copies, and the preparatory stage of laboratory work can be regarded as complete.

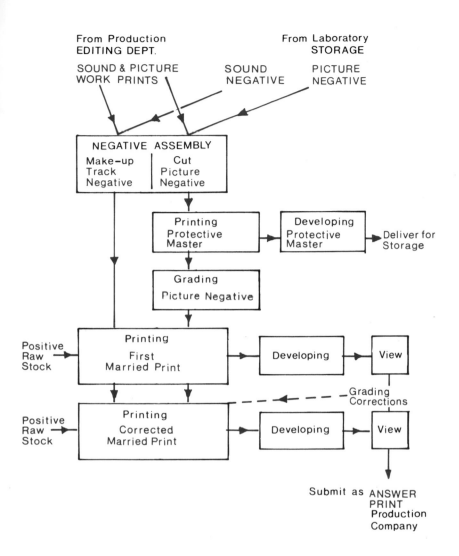

From Production
EDITING DEPT.

SOUND & PICTURE
WORK PRINTS

From Laboratory
STORAGE

SOUND
NEGATIVE

PICTURE
NEGATIVE

NEGATIVE ASSEMBLY

Make-up
Track
Negative

Cut
Picture
Negative

Printing
Protective
Master

Developing
Protective
Master

Deliver for
Storage

Grading
Picture Negative

Positive
Raw
Stock

Printing
First
Married Print

Developing

View

Grading
Corrections

Positive
Raw
Stock

Printing
Corrected
Married Print

Developing

View

Submit as ANSWER
PRINT
Production
Company

ANSWER PRINT PREPARATION   The Laboratory assembles the final picture
and track negative to match the Editor's work print, so that an Answer Print can
be sent for approval.

Release Print Manufacture

By the time release print manufacture is undertaken, the printing characteristics for both picture and sound have been standardised and the processing requirement is to make the necessary number of copies of consistent quality to match the approved answer print. When a large number of prints are called for it is not now usual for them to be made direct from the original picture negative, because of possible damage during repeated use on high-speed printing machines. Bulk release printing will therefore be carried out from a duplicate negative, often known as a production dupe, which can be replaced if necessary. Such duplicate negatives can now be made as colour reversal intermediates (CRI) at a single step direct from the original without appreciable loss of image quality and can be printed to incorporate the finally approved scene-to-scene grading of the answer print. Where a very large number of identical copies are called for, second duplicates may be made so that multiple prints can be produced rapidly. The use of duplicate negatives or CRI's is of course also necessary when release prints are required with a different format of image or a different gauge of film from the original. For change of gauge, a corresponding sound track negative will be re-recorded from the original magnetic master.

Release print operations often integrate printing and developing at high-speed for maximum output. Prints are inspected, usually by projection on a small screen, but the viewer at this stage is not required to assess scene-to-scene grading, which has previously been set at answer printing.

Despatch preparation

Following inspection, release prints may require final make-up assembly before despatch; this can include the addition of distribution trade-marks and censor certificate titles and individual reels may be joined into larger rolls for projection convenience. At this stage individual prints are given their copy number identification for the distributor's records before despatch.

Final film handling operations on release prints may include edge-waxing or lubrication to ensure satisfactory projection, anti-scratch treatment and protection for longer print life and, in the case of narrow-gauge copies, mounting on special reels or in cassettes for use on certain types of projection equipment.

14

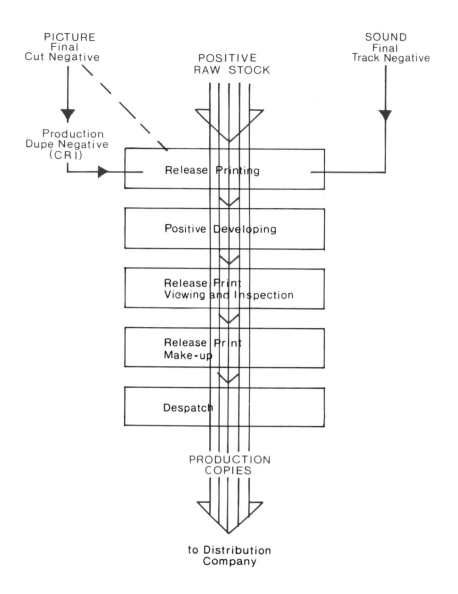

PICTURE
Final
Cut Negative

POSITIVE
RAW STOCK

SOUND
Final
Track Negative

Production
Dupe Negative
(CRI)

Release Printing

Positive Developing

Release Print
Viewing and Inspection

Release Print
Make-up

Despatch

PRODUCTION
COPIES

to Distribution
Company

RELEASE PRINT MANUFACTURE After Answer Print approval, the
Laboratory will be required to make a number of copies for general distribution
and public showing.

Types of Film

The photographic films in use in the motion picture industry can be divided into those used for making the original exposure in the camera and those for making prints of one type or another in the laboratory; in each of these main groups both black-and-white and colour film stocks are available.

Camera original materials

There are two basic types: (i) negative film stocks, which after developing yield a negative image, whose tonal distribution is the opposite of the original scene, and (ii) reversal film stocks, which after processing show a positive type of image, whose tones are similar to the actual scene. Reversal stocks are made with characteristics either suitable for direct projection of the original, as is usual in amateur cinematography, or suitable for printing on to another reversal stock to make copies, which is the professional usage. Negative films are of course unsuitable for actual projection and are intended for producing copies by printing on to a corresponding positive material.

Print materials

These are either positive films, for printing from original negatives, or reversal print films for copying reversal originals. In addition, a laboratory uses a number of other materials, negative and reversal, which yield intermediate positives and duplicate negatives for various purposes.

All motion-picture film consists of a light-sensitive layer, known as the emulsion, coated on a transparent support, the base, which is usually a derivative of cellulose (triacetate or polyester).

Black and white films normally have only one layer, which after exposure and processing yields a monochrome image of varying concentrations of metallic silver grains. In colour films, on the other hand, the base carries three separate emulsion layers, which are individually sensitive to red, green and blue light. During processing, the images in the exposed film are changed to transparent dyes which are seen superimposed as a colour picture.

In a colour reversal film the image produced on processing is a positive one corresponding to the original scene both in tone and hue. In a colour negative, however, the image is opposite to the original in tone and complementary in colour. Thus a white object appears dark on the film, while a black one light. Green grass appears reddish-purple on the negative, a blue sky is yellow-orange while a red car would form a bluish-green image. When the colour negative is printed on to a corresponding colour positive film, the resulting image represents both the tones and hues of the original scene.

16

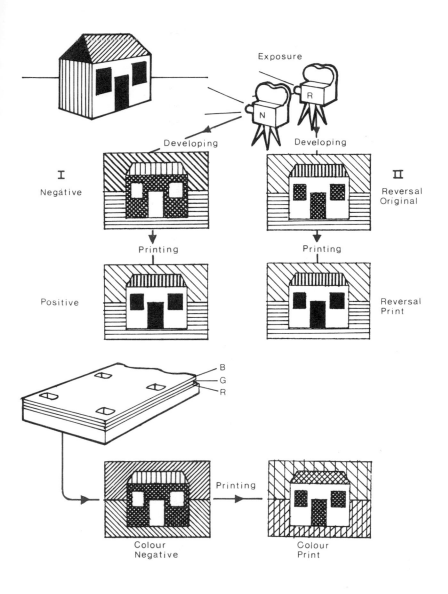

I	**II**
Negative	Reversal Original
Positive	Reversal Print

Colour Negative

Colour Print

TYPES OF FILM Original film in the camera can be either Negative (I) or Reversal (II) types. In colour materials three separate layers on a single base record the Red, Green and Blue components of the scene.

17

Film Gauges

The various gauges of film which may be found in use are normally specified by the width of the strip measured in millimetres. The size most used for professional motion picture work for some sixty years is *35mm* wide, but the narrow gauge *16mm* film, originally used only by amateurs, is now extensively used for many applications. A narrower gauge of *8mm* is practically universal for home movies and even this size is being applied for industrial and educational purposes and in television. The demands for wide-screen presentation in large cinema theatres led to the introduction of a film stock *70mm* in width, although its application is limited to specialised performances rather than general distribution. Other gauges both wider (*55mm*, *65mm*) and narrower (*9·5mm*) than the 35mm standard have been in use at various times, but are now regarded as obsolete.

Perforations

The size, shape, position and pitch of the perforation holes along the edges of the strip of film are specifically matched to various types of camera and printer mechanisms, so it is important for both the gauge and perforation details to be identified. 35mm film is always perforated with two rows of holes along the edges but three shapes of hole are in regular use; these are

Bell and Howell (BH) known internationally as N (for Negative)
Kodak Standard (KS) known internationally as P (for Positive)
and Cinemascope (CS).

Two pitch dimensions are to be found, the standard having perforation spacing of 0·1870" (4·75mm) and the short pitch with an interval of 0·1866" (4·74mm). Negative stocks are normally made with B & H holes of short pitch, positive stocks of the KS type, standard pitch. There is only one type of hole on 16mm film but this gauge may be perforated along one or both edges, with standard pitch 0·3000" (7·62mm) or short pitch, 0·2994" (7·605mm). 8mm stock can have two very different perforations, the original form, now known as Regular 8 or 8mm Type R, with perforations of the same size and shape as 16mm but with a pitch of 0·1500" (3·81mm), and Super-8 or 8mm Type S, with a smaller hole with an interval of 0·1667" (4·234mm).

To facilitate laboratory bulk production of narrow gauge release prints, film stocks are manufactured with two or more rows of 16mm or 8mm perforations. They are slit after processing to produce two or four narrow gauge prints.

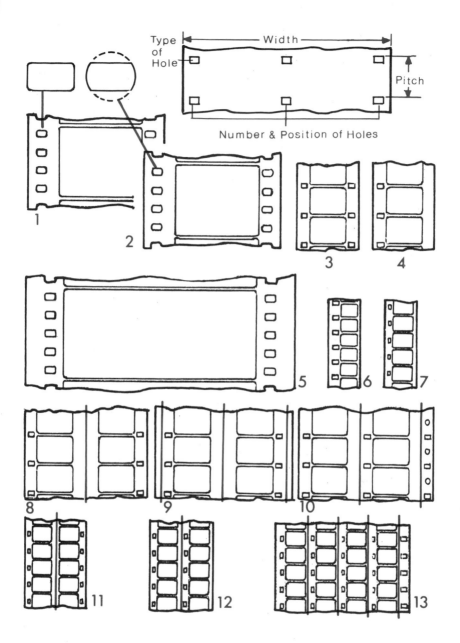

FILM GAUGES Film gauges are specified by width, type of perforation hole, perforation pitch and number of rows of holes. Examples shown are:—
(1) 35mm Positive. (2) 35mm Negative. (3) 16mm Camera Film. (4) 16mm Print Film. (5) 70mm Print Film. (6) Regular 8mm. (7) Super-8.
(8) Double 16 on 32mm. (9) Double 16 on 35mm, 1–4. (10) Double 16 on 35mm, 1–3–0. (11) Double Super-8, 1–4. (12) Double Super-8, 1–3.
(13) Four row Super-8 on 35mm.

Film Manufacture and Identification

Motion picture film is manufactured in wide rolls, known as 'jumbo rolls' or parent rolls, up to 60 inches wide and 2600 feet or more in length, which are subsequently slit to the required width and cut to the required length. The roll of film in the can finally delivered to the customer will be identified on its label as follows:

Manufacturer's Description and Product Type Number: e.g. Colour Print Stock Type 7281.

Emulsion Batch Number: the particular emulsion mix which will be coated on several wide rolls.

Roll Number: the identification of the particular wide parent roll.

Strip Number: the parent roll is slit into a number of strips each given its own reference number, usually from 1 to 36 for 35mm width and from 1 to 70 for 16mm.

Roll Cut Number: if the length of 2000 or 2400 feet originally coated is packed in shorter lengths, the first length is called cut 1 and so on. For example if the final lengths are 400 feet from a 2000 foot parent there will be cut numbers 1–5.

Perforation and winding details

The type of perforation, the manner of winding and the type of core will also be indicated on the can label. Some types of camera film, especially 16mm, are wound on daylight loading spools for direct use in the camera and both the type of spool and winding will be indicated.

These identification details, are of real importance to the laboratory. The film gauge determines what processing and printing machines must be used and the product type number specifies the developing system required. The emulsion number allows the photographic characteristics of the stock to be identified and all the parent rolls of the same emulsion number can be expected to be identical or very similar.

The length of the roll of raw stock and the type of winding must be known by the camera assistant loading the magazine. Film with perforations along both edges symmetrically, as on 35mm and the 2R type of 16mm, is identified as wound emulsion side outwards or inwards. Film with perforations on one edge only, particularly 16mm 1R-2994 or 1R-3000, are described as Winding A or Winding B.

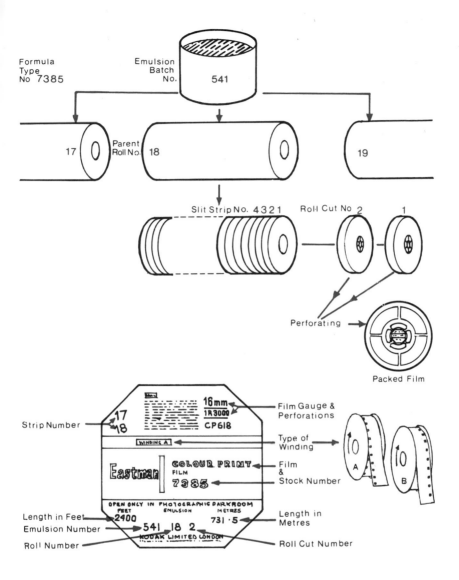

FILM MANUFACTURE AND IDENTIFICATION The label on a can of raw stock identifies the type, gauge and quantity and provides details of its manufacturing history.

21

Stock Edge Numbers

It is often necessary in editing and cutting to identify and record a particular individual frame of the negative without ambiguity. This location is based on the series of numbers placed by the manufacturer at regular intervals along the edge of all camera films, both negative and reversal, and known as stock numbers, key numbers, edge numbers or footage numbers. In black and white film these numbers are printed in ink on the base surface of the film and can be seen on the raw stock, but in colour materials, they are photographically exposed during manufacture and only become visible after the film has been processed; these are latent image edge numbers. After development, the image on negative stocks appears as a dark figure on the clear background of the unexposed film but on reversal materials the numbers are light on a black margin.

On 35mm film the edge numbers occur at intervals of 64 perforations, corresponding to 16 frames or one foot, and are therefore correctly described as 'footage numbers'. 16mm film, on the other hand, may show edge numbers at 16, 20 or 40 perforation intervals, every 16, 20 or 40 frames, but these are still often termed 'footage numbers'. The first symbols in the group usually are a code for the product type and the remaining figures are the actual footage numbers, increasing by one at specified intervals.

Identifying the position of a frame
A particular frame of the exposed film can be specifically identified as the 'nth' frame before or after the nearest footage number; however, since the full series of digits of the type 'E2X 0993457' can extend over two or even three frames it is essential to indicate which is taken as the starting point or 'zero' by underlining or 'boxing' the particular group of digits which are opposite the zero frame, thus E2X, E2X, 457, etc. Where no 'box' is indicated it is usual practice to assume that the last variable numbers of the group are opposite the zero frame.

A frame can be identified as after a given number: 457 plus 12 frames, written 457 + 12, or before the next number: 4 frames before 458, 458 minus 4 frames or 458 – 4. The minus sign can however be ambiguous and is sometimes read merely as a dash, so that the identification as 457 + 12 is preferable unless the information is written in full '4 frames before 458'.

Negative stock loaded in the camera directly as supplied will show the footage numbers increasing from the beginning to the end of the roll. If however the stock has been rewound before use, the highest number will occur at the start and the numbers will decrease from the beginning. When this occurs it is especially important to verify the frame identification count as plus or minus.

It is of course essential that all rush prints shall have an image of the negative numbers printed through for subsequent matching.

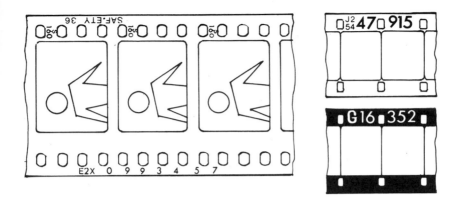

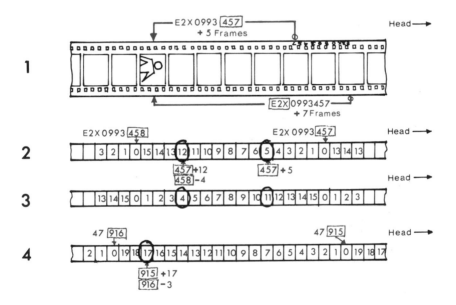

STOCK EDGE NUMBERS Sequential numbers printed on the edge of the film during manufacture allow individual frames to be exactly identified, but the zero frame must be clearly indicated (1). A frame may be located as either after or before an edge number (2) but if the stock has been rewound before exposure, the numbers run in reverse sequence (3). 16mm film may have numbers at 20 or even 40 frame intervals (4), 35mm film always at 16 frames.

Image Formats

The proportions of the picture image on a frame of film or projected on a cinema screen are specified by the ratio of its width to height, which is termed the aspect ratio, A.R. For many years from the beginning of the century, the frame most widely adopted had the proportions 4 units wide by 3 units high, an aspect ratio of 4:3 or 1·33:1. After 1955 there was a marked trend towards wider screens in cinema theatres, although in general the height available could not be increased. The so-called 'wide-screen' image is now almost universal for 35mm entertainment films, generally with aspect ratios between 1·65:1 and 1·85:1, but the original ratio 1·33:1 has been retained in television use and also is general on the narrow gauge films, 16mm, Regular-8mm and Super-8.

The move towards wide-screen presentation was given its initial impetus by the introduction of the Cinemascope system in 1953; in this, a laterally-compressed image was photographed on 35mm film using anamorphic lenses, which had a reduction factor greater horizontally than vertically. On projecting this 'squeezed' image through a similar lens, the distortion was corrected and a picture with the very wide aspect ratio of 2·35:1 obtained on the screen.

Wide gauge film
70mm prints have an aspect ratio of 2·2:1 and although originally obtained by printing from a similar large negative image on film 65mm wide, they are now generally made by anamorphic enlargement printing from a 35mm original of the 'squeezed' cinemascope type.

In order to use film stock more economically in original photography, a number of systems using small images for enlargement printing have been introduced. One of these was Techniscope, in which a half-size 35mm frame two perforations high is exposed in the camera and anamorphically printed to give a cinemascope type 35mm print.

16mm originals can be enlarged to give standard 35mm prints but the normal 16mm frame proportions are ineffectively used for wide-screen formats. An increased 16mm frame size, known as Super-16, was therefore introduced which allows a wide-screen 35mm print of A.R. 1·65 to be produced from a larger area on the 16mm film, with a resulting improvement in quality.

24

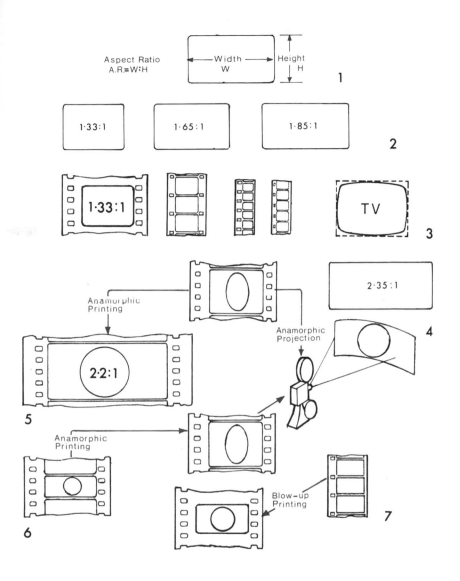

IMAGE FORMATS   The aspect ratio of a picture is the ratio of its width to height (1). Wide screen pictures have A.R. 1.65:1 or 1.85:1 (2) but 1.33:1 is used for T.V. and narrow-gauge films (3). Anamorphic photography gives a "squeezed" image which is expanded on projection to A.R. 2.35:1 (4) or can be enlarged to a 70mm print (5). Techniscope half-frame photography (6) can be printed to give a squeezed image. Super-16 photography allows enlargement to widescreen 35mm (7).

25

A Wind & B Wind: Emulsion Positions

As noted earlier, rolls of raw stock which have perforations down one edge only may be supplied for use in two different windings, called A Wind or B Wind. The same terms have become used to describe the emulsion position of 16mm prints on projection and hence that of other films, irrespective of whether there are one or two rows of perforations. Popular usage is confusing and if not understood can lead to errors.

16mm film run in a camera must always be exposed with its emulsion surface towards the lens, whether it is negative or reversal material. If the processed frame is held so that the picture appears correct—top of the scene at the top, right hand side of the scene on the right, titles reading from left to right—it will be found that the BASE side of the film is towards the observer. This is called the 'B' wind characteristic.

When a normal print is made from a camera original, the emulsion side of the print stock is exposed in contact with the emulsion side of the original. The resultant image after processing will be found to read correctly when viewed with the EMULSION side towards the observer: this is termed the 'A' wind position.

Projection
If a camera original, such as Kodachrome film, is projected it must be run through the projector in the same way as it was wound in the camera: emulsion side to the lens, base side to the projector lamp. Films with the 'B' wind image characteristic are thus always projected 'Emulsion to Lens'.

A contact print made from a camera original, on the other hand, must be projected the other way round, base side to lens, emulsion side to lamp: 'A' wind films thus always run 'Emulsion to Lamp'. This explains why it is unsatisfactory to join together camera originals and contact prints in one roll for projection or printing because of the differing emulsion positions throughout.

To summarise:
Original Negative is 'B' wind
Contact Print from Negative is 'A' wind
Original Reversal is 'B' wind
Contact Reversal Print is 'A' wind.
But Duplicate Internegative from Original Reversal is also 'A' wind and a Contact Print from this is 'B' wind, like the original.

The photographic 16mm sound track negatives must match the picture material with which they will be printed; thus the track to go with a picture original negative or reversal must be 'B' wind, while that for a picture internegative would be 'A' wind.

26

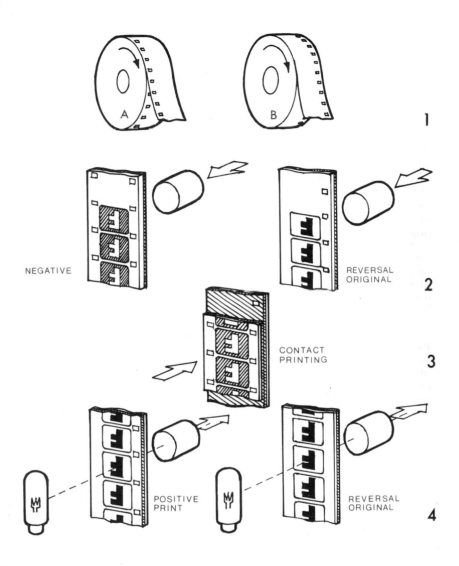

NEGATIVE

REVERSAL ORIGINAL

1

2

CONTACT PRINTING

3

POSITIVE PRINT

REVERSAL ORIGINAL

4

A WIND AND B WIND   With the emulsion side inwards and the roll unwinding clockwise, the perforation holes are on the nearer edge in A winding and on the further edge for B winding (1). 16mm camera films are exposed emulsion side towards the lens (2) and the image is termed "B wind." In contact printing (3) the emulsion surfaces are together, so a contact print must be projected emulsion side towards the lamp, "A wind," whereas the "B wind" reversal original projects emulsion to lens (4).

27

The B & W Negative & Positive Process

In the photographic process an image is formed as the result of the action of light on the components of a sensitive layer. In its simplest form, this is a layer of gelatine emulsion containing minute grains of silver compounds, usually bromides or iodides, known as Halides. When exposed in the camera, the varying intensities of light in the image formed by the lens affect a number of these grains. Where the scene photographed is brightest, in the whites and high-lights, most light will reach the film and the largest number of grains will be affected, while in blacks and shadow areas, few if any grains will be reached.

At this stage, the changes in the grains are not visible and the image in the emulsion is termed 'latent' (hidden). However, if the film is then treated with suitable chemicals, the latent image grains are converted to particles of black metallic silver and made visible, while the unexposed grains are unchanged. This process is known as development.

These unexposed grains can then be dissolved away by other chemicals in the fixing process, so that after washing to remove chemical residues and drying the film we obtain an image in which the light areas of the original scene are represented by large concentrations of silver grains while the dark areas have comparatively few. The tonal distribution of the scene is thus inverted, light to dark, and this image is termed a black-and-white negative.

Print making

In making a print, the negative is used to modulate the uniform light of the printing machine reaching the light-sensitive emulsion of the positive film stock. Where the concentration of silver in the negative is greatest, the printing light intensity will be greatly reduced and only a few grains in the positive emulsion will be affected. Conversely, where the negative is lightest a greater amount of printing light will pass and a large number of positive grains will be exposed.

Development of the latent image so formed produces an image whose light and shade distribution is opposite to that of the negative and which thus corresponds to that of the original scene. This is the positive print which, when projected on a cinema screen, provides a representation of the scene originally photographed.

Although the photographic principles are similar, negative and positive film stocks must be processed through different developing solutions. Negative materials are highly sensitive to allow photography with minimum available light, and are processed to a low contrast to ensure accurate graduation over a wide tonal range. Positive stocks are made with very fine grain structure, allowing the image to be greatly magnified on projection. They are not very sensitive, as the printing light sources are strong, and are developed to a high contrast to give the greatest tonal range on projection.

28

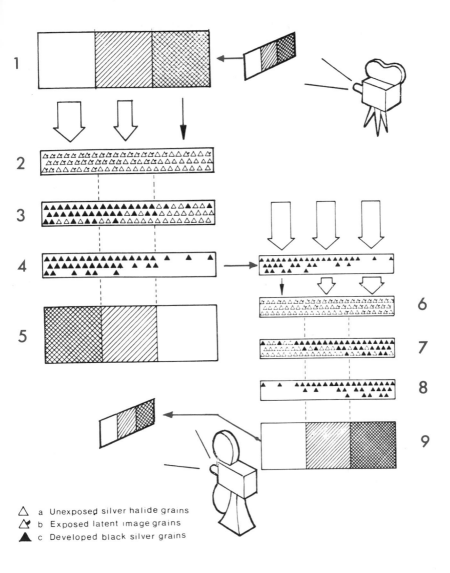

△ a Unexposed silver halide grains
◬ b Exposed latent image grains
▲ c Developed black silver grains

BLACK AND WHITE NEGATIVE AND POSITIVE Varying amounts of light
from the scene (1) fall on the film in the camera and produce changes
in some of the silver halide grains (2). In developing (3) these are converted
to silver and the unexposed grains removed by fixing (4). The resultant image
is the Negative (5), with its tonal distribution opposite to that of the scene.
In printing, this negative image modulates the printing light so that different
exposures are formed in the positive print stock (6). After development (7)
and fixing (8) the Positive image (9) has a similar tonal distribution to the
original scene.

29

The B & W Reversal Process

Certain black and white film stocks can be processed in such a way that the resultant image has the same tonal distribution as the original subject, so that the camera film can be projected to represent the scene without the need for a separate printing operation. These 'reversal' films are exposed in the camera to form a latent image in the same way as black-and-white negative stock and the first stage of processing is to develop this latent image to black grains of metallic silver.

Reversal exposure
At the next stage, these developed silver grains are bleached and dissolved away, leaving a residue of the silve halide grains not originally exposed. These grains are now exposed to light, or chemically treated to have the same effect, and a second developing stage converts them to metallic silver. After fixing and drying, the tones of resultant image on the film correspond to those of the original and it is thus a positive image suitable for projection. The term 'reversal' refers to the transformation from negative image to positive during the processing sequence.

Copying reversal images
Copies of reversal original films can be made by printing on to a similar type of stock and processing again by reversal, so that the print has the same tonal character as the original from which it was made.

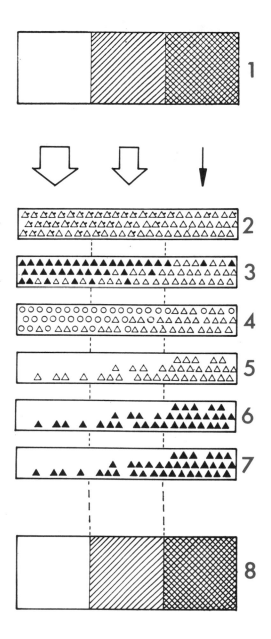

BLACK-AND-WHITE REVERSAL   Variations in light from the original scene (1) produce a latent image (2) in the camera film. This is developed to black silver grains (3) which are then bleached (4) and dissolved away (5). The remaining silver halide grains are developed (6) and fixed (7) to produce an image having the same tonal distribution as the original scene (8).

For colour you must record red, green and blue information.

The Colour Negative & Positive Process

The essential feature of modern methods of colour cinematography is the formation of latent images in three separate layers of light-sensitive emulsions coated on a single base. The three emulsions are made individually responsive to red light, green light and blue light respectively, so that latent images formed at any point are determined by the quantities of the red, green and blue components in the light reaching it from the corresponding area in the scene photographed. In the course of processing, the latent images are converted to transparent dye images of the complementary colours, cyan (blue-green), magenta (red-purple) and yellow, which produce the resultant colour picture.

Colour negatives
The first development converts the exposed grains to black metallic silver and at the same time components of the emulsion called 'couplers' form a coloured image around each silver grain. These coloured images are formed only around the exposed grains; unexposed grains are not affected, and are completely removed by a fixing solution, as in black and white processing. The remaining developed black silver grains are then chemically bleached and dissolved away by a second fixing solution. This leaves only the coloured image in the three layers, forming the colour negative: the picture is a negative both in its tonal distribution of light and shade and in its colour reproduction, the hues of the subject being represented by their complementaries.

Colour prints
Colour prints suitable for projection are made by copying on to a similar multi-layer positive stock. The areas of the negative modulate the uniform printing light both in intensity and in colour, so that varying latent images are formed in the three colour-sensitive layers of the print film. Processing of this latent image produces a coloured image in the three layers which make up the colour picture. This has a tonal distribution corresponding to that of the original subject and the hues of the scene are represented in their correct sense.

As in black-and-white practice, negative and positive colour stocks are considerably different and require different developing solutions. Negative stocks have high sensitivity, low contrast and wide latitude to accept a considerable range of exposures. (In most colour negative materials, the image is coloured dominantly orange-yellow by 'Masking' components, which improve the purity of colour rendering in the resultant prints.) Colour positive stocks have very fine grain structure, are comparatively less sensitive and are of higher contrast and colour saturation.

32

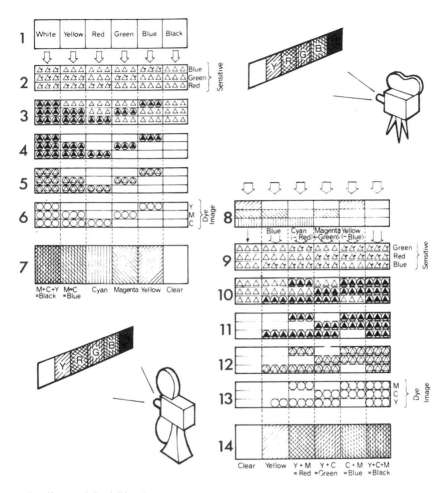

White	Yellow	Red	Green	Blue	Black

1

2 — Blue / Green / Red — Sensitive

3

4

5

6 — Y / M / C — Dye Image

7

M+C+Y = Black   M+C = Blue   Cyan   Magenta   Yellow   Clear

8 — Blue   Cyan (= Red)   Magenta (= Green)   Yellow (= Blue)

9 — Green / Red / Blue — Sensitive

10

11

12

13 — M / C / Y — Dye Image

14 — Clear   Yellow   Y + M = Red   Y + C = Green   C + M = Blue   Y+C+M = Black

△   Unexposed silver halide grains
△   Exposed silver halide grains (latent image)
●   Developed silver grains with associated colour image
○   Colour image only

COLOUR NEGATIVE AND POSITIVE   Coloured light from the original scene (1) produces latent images in the three emulsion layers of the negative in the camera (2). When developed (3) complementary colour images are formed in each layer wherever a black silver grain is produced. Fixing (4) removes unexposed silver halides and the silver image is bleached (5) and fixed out (6), leaving a dye image which is a colour negative (7) of the original scene. In printing, the light from the printer passing through this negative (8) exposes the positive film (9). The latent images so formed are developed to complementary colour images in the three emulsion layers (10). Fixing (11), bleaching (12) and a second fix (13) leaves a dye image, which is a positive (14) corresponding to the original scene.

33

The Colour Reversal Process

Some multi-layer colour film stocks are made for reversal processing to give a positive image on the film exposed in the camera. As with a colour negative material, light passing through the camera lens forms latent images in the three colour-sensitive layers of the film, but the first step in processing is to develop these latent images to black metallic silver without any colour coupling taking place. The remaining halide grains in all layers are then exposed to light or correspondingly chemically treated, and by a second development stage converted to silver with associated complementary dye images formed by colour coupling. The whole of the silver image from both development stages is then removed by bleaching and fixing, leaving only the colour in the three layers. The resultant picture has thus the tonal character and hue representation of the original scene and is a colour positive.

Camera reversal films

Colour reversal materials for original photography are of two main types, one having a high contrast and colour saturation suitable for projection itself, and the other of lower contrast intended for making copies by printing on to a similar reversal type film.

Direct reversal prints can be made from both types of reversal originals, but the print stock must be correctly matched to the original characteristic. For example, the high contrast original Ektachrome EF must be printed on the matching lower contrast stock, Ektachrome R Print. Similarly, the low contrast original Ektachrome Commercial must be printed on the corresponding higher contrast Eastman Reversal Colour Print Film.

A stock is also made specially for the duplication of colour negative films at one operation by direct printing and reversal processing; this is known as Colour Reversal Intermediate, usually shortened to CRI.

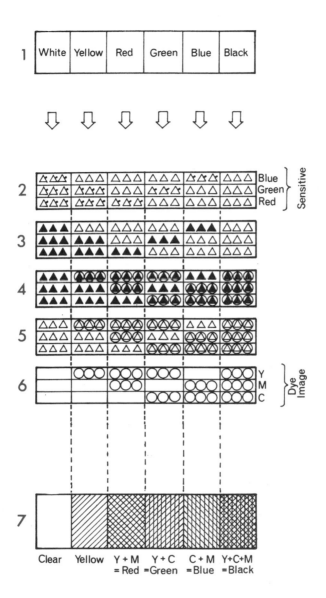

| 1 | White | Yellow | Red | Green | Blue | Black |

2 Blue / Green / Red } Sensitive

3

4

5

6 Y / M / C } Dye Image

7

| Clear | Yellow | Y + M = Red | Y + C = Green | C + M = Blue | Y+C+M = Black |

COLOUR REVERSAL The latent image formed in the camera film (2) by coloured light from the original scene (1), is first developed to black silver grains (3). In the second (colour) developer the remaining silver halide grains are developed to produce complementary colour images in each layer wherever any of these grains is converted to silver (4). The silver grains from both development stages are bleached (5) and fixed out (6) to leave a positive dye image (7) representing the original scene.

35

Processing Machines

All modern processing machines are continuous, the film passing as a continuously moving strip from one solution to the next. It follows a flat spiral path over a series of pulleys or rollers mounted on spindles four to six feet apart on a frame, the whole assembly being termed a rack. Each rack is immersed in a tank of solution, the time of each step of the process being determined by the length of the film path on the rack and the speed at which the film is driven through the machine. Where longer times are required in a particular solution, several racks may be enclosed within one tank.

The film must be moved through the machine smoothly at a uniform rate without any undue strain on the strip, and complex demand-drive systems are now general to ensure consistently low tension throughout the whole path. In some machines the strip is driven by rotating sprocket rolls whose teeth engage with the film perforation holes.

Sprocketless processors

Sprocket-drive machines are restricted to a particular film size and perforation pattern and recently sprocket-less drives using plastic tyres or ribbed or dimpled rollers have become widespread. Such friction-driven machines can handle different widths of film and perforation sizes without change and are specially suitable for processing original camera material, avoiding possible mechanical damage from sprocket teeth.

Light must of course be prevented from reaching the film while it is being fed into the machine and during most of the processing steps. But after the fixing operation the film is no longer light-sensitive, so the final stages of washing and drying can be completed in the light. Some processing machines are therefore divided by a wall through which the film path passes from the dark room side to the light side.

In 'daylight' developing machines which can be housed in a lighted room, the first series of tanks are covered by light-tight hoods under which the film passes from rack to rack. The film is fed into the machine from enclosed magazines, similar to those used in the camera, and only a very short length of film at the end of a roll is exposed to light when one roll is joined on to the next.

When an original camera negative is known to be seriously under-exposed as a result of inadequate light, the results can often be improved by extra development time ('forced developing'). To provide this, the laboratory must make changes to the processing machine, either increasing the film path in the tank or running the machine more slowly. It is therefore essential to check with the laboratory in advance that such a service is available and to mark very clearly exactly which rolls of exposed negative are to be so treated.

36

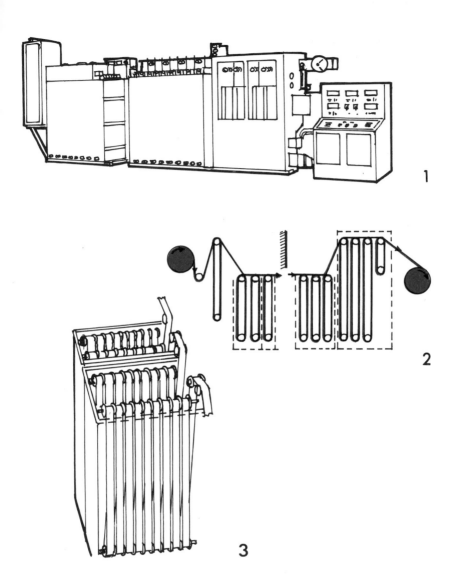

PROCESSING MACHINES   In a developing machine (1), the film passes
continuously through a series of chemical solutions contained in separate
tanks until the final drying cabinets, after which it is wound up on a spool (2).
In each tank the film passes in a flat spiral path over a series of pulleys on a
frame called a rack (3).

You needn't know the chemistry but it helps to know the sequence.

Negative Processing Equipment

Processing black-and-white materials is comparatively simple and the machines used need only a few tanks and racks. The film first passes through the developing solution, usually for about 5 to 10 minutes at a temperature of 70°F (21°C); then follows a stop bath and wash to terminate the developing action; then the fixing solution, usually for 5 minutes or so; a wash in water for 6 to 8 minutes and finally the film is dried in enclosed dust-free cabinets.

For colour negative, more solution tanks are required and the overall processing time is longer. Some colour negative stocks have an anti-halation backing and this must be removed, usually by softening in a special solution, washing the backing layer off and scrubbing the base surface to remove the last traces. The film then passes to the colour developer solution where (in 12 to 14 minutes) the latent image is converted to silver and the associated dye image; then a brief spray rinse removes traces of developer solution before the film passes to the first fixing stage. After the unused halides have been removed, the film goes through a further wash and enters the bleach solution. Another wash and the film enters the second fixing bath at which the bleached silver component is removed. The final washing which follows must be very thorough, since traces of processing chemicals can cause the image to fade. Passage through a final stabilizer solution is necessary to ensure a permanent image, with a brief rinse and the application of a wetting agent to eliminate water droplets on the surface of the film as it enters the drying cabinet.

This whole sequence involves some fourteen steps and a total time of the order of one hour from beginning to end. For even a moderate running speed of 3000 feet an hour a colour negative developing machine with a length of 100 feet in each rack will require some 26 racks in solution tanks and perhaps 8 in the dry box.

Higher speed processing
The need for a shorter processing sequence to permit the use of smaller machines of high output has been recognised and in 1973 a new colour negative type was introduced by Eastman Kodak to this end. This has a hardened emulsion and can be safely processed at a temperature of 100° to 106°F (38°–41°C) against the previous 70°F. In combination with revised chemical formulae, this allows colour developing to be completed in 3 minutes and the whole process, including drying, in about 20 minutes. A developing machine for this process thus needs only 15 solution racks of 100 foot capacity for an output rate of 6000 feet per hour. It must be noted that this shortened high-temperature process can only be applied to the film for which it was designed.

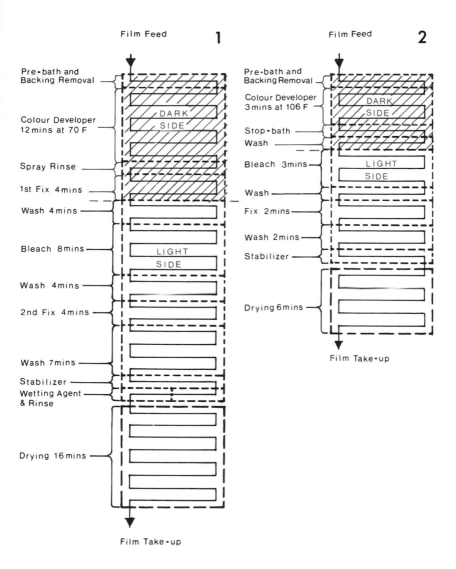

Film Feed **1**

Pre-bath and Backing Removal

Colour Developer 12 mins at 70 F

DARK SIDE

Spray Rinse

1st Fix 4 mins

Wash 4 mins

Bleach 8 mins

LIGHT SIDE

Wash 4 mins

2nd Fix 4 mins

Wash 7 mins

Stabilizer
Wetting Agent & Rinse

Drying 16 mins

Film Take-up

Film Feed **2**

Pre-bath and Backing Removal

Colour Developer 3 mins at 106 F

DARK SIDE

Stop-bath
Wash

Bleach 3 mins

LIGHT SIDE

Wash

Fix 2 mins

Wash 2 mins

Stabilizer

Drying 6 mins

Film Take-up

COLOUR NEGATIVE PROCESSING SEQUENCE (1) Standard process ECN-1 at 70°F (21°C), total time approximately 61 minutes. For an output of 3000 feet per hour, running at 50 feet per minute, the machine requires 26 solution tank racks holding up to 100 feet each and 8 racks in the Drying Cabinet.
(2) High Speed Process ECN-2 at 100°–106°F (38–41°C). Higher temperature reduces the total time, and a much shorter machine with 15 solution racks and 5 drying racks of 100 feet each can be run at 100 feet per minute.

Reversal Processing Equipment

Even for black-and-white materials, the reversal process is a complex one since the originally exposed image has to be removed by bleaching; and a new one formed from the previously unused silver halides, either chemically, or by exposing them to light.

The stages comprise:

> First Developer/Bleach/Clear
> Second Developer/Fix/Dry
> with a wash between each stage.

For colour reversal film, the sequence is somewhat similar but the first developer forms a black-and-white image only and the removal of the silver by bleaching and fixing is deferred until after the colour image has been formed in the second developer.

Colour reversal processing

Colour reversal processing has been greatly speeded up by using higher temperatures [100° to 110°F (38°–43°C)] but these necessitate hardening the emulsion so that it can withstand these temperatures without softening or even melting.

The first step in such a colour reversal process is to pass the film through a pre-hardening bath for some $2\frac{1}{2}$ minutes, and this solution must be removed and neutralised before the film enters the first developer. At 100°F the time here can be as short as 3 minutes, and is followed by a brief stop bath and wash. The film then passes to the second (colour) developer, for a period of some $3\frac{1}{2}$ minutes at 110°C, again followed by stop bath and wash. The whole silver image from both development stages is then bleached, the film washed again, and the bleached silver removed by fixing. After a final wash and a stabilising bath the operation is completed by drying, the whole sequence taking some 25 minutes.

Colour reversal materials for original photography are normally limited to 16mm films but a colour reversal intermediate (CRI) is now widely used in the laboratory for making direct duplicate negatives in both 35mm and 16mm.

Many original reversal stocks are suitable for forced development if under-exposed, the additional developing time being given in the first developer. A very considerable increase in effective photographic speed rating can be obtained, but if carried to extremes the result will show a very coarse grained image. Laboratories can therefore offer several stages of forced development. Film requiring special developing conditions must always be sent in on separate rolls appropriately identified; usually the processing is indicated by giving the ASA speed rating at which the film was actually exposed.

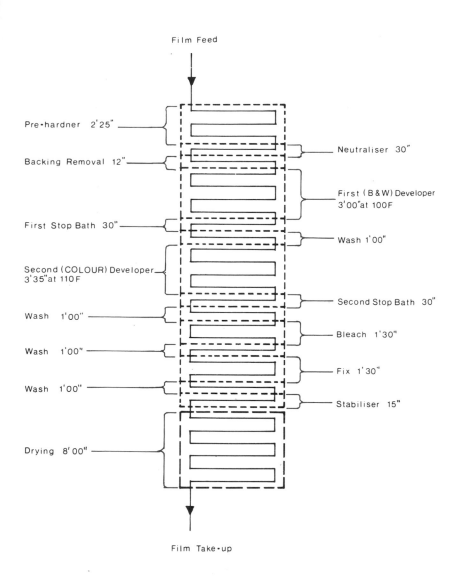

Film Feed

Pre·hardner 2'25"

Backing Removal 12"

First Stop Bath 30"

Second (COLOUR) Developer 3'35"at 110F

Wash 1'00"

Wash 1'00"

Wash 1'00"

Drying 8'00"

Neutraliser 30"

First (B&W) Developer 3'00"at 100F

Wash 1'00"

Second Stop Bath 30"

Bleach 1'30"

Fix 1'30"

Stabiliser 15"

Film Take·up

COLOUR REVERSAL PROCESSING SEQUENCE Reversal processing is carried out at high temperatures (95–110°F) to keep machine length short. This shows a machine with 24 solution tank racks of capacity up to 75 feet of 16mm film each. The overall process time is 24 minutes and the output some 4500 feet per hour. The first developer tank has capacity for increased developing time ("forced development").

41

Printing Machines

The second main group of specialised machines in the laboratory are those used for printing, in which a strip of raw stock, usually a positive material, is exposed through a processed image, usually an original negative or reversal, by light under carefully controlled conditions. Printing machines may be divided into contact and optical printers, according to the image relation between the negative and the raw stock. In the former, the original being printed and the stock to be exposed are held closely in contact at the moment of exposure with the two emulsion surfaces together.

In an optical printer, the two films are separated and an illuminated image of the negative is formed on the emulsion surface of the raw stock by a lens, much as in a camera. There is no need for any standard relation between the two emulsion surfaces and the two films can be of the different formats.

Printer types are also divided by the manner in which the two films are moved, either continuously or one frame at a time, as in a camera. The latter are termed Intermittent or Step Printers.

All printing machines are thus comprised in four groups:

(a) *CONTINUOUS CONTACT PRINTERS.* This is the most widely used group for making both rush prints and normal release prints both colour and black-and-white, picture and sound; they can run at high speeds under automatic control but the gauge and format of original and print stock must of course be the same.

(b) *CONTINUOUS OPTICAL PRINTERS.* These are a comparatively recent development, more or less restricted to reduction copying, for example making 8mm release prints from a 16mm original.

(c) *CONTACT STEP PRINTERS.* These are used in the laboratory when a print having a very steady image in exact registration with the original is required, as for back-projection plates, titles and special effects, and colour separation records.

(d) *OPTICAL STEP PRINTERS.* This term covers a very varied group of printing machines for special purposes. The simplest are those used for reduction copying, for example from 35mm originals to 16mm, but extremely elaborate optical printers with facilities for running several negatives simultaneously and with a wide range of image size and position adjustments form an essential part of special effects work.

Sound tracks cannot of course be printed on step printer mechanisms.

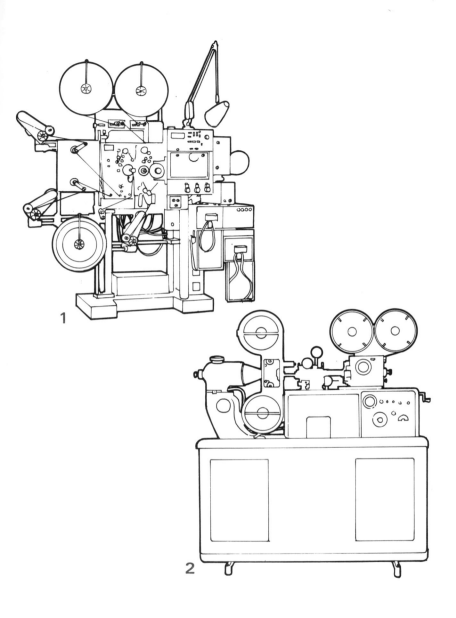

PRINTING MACHINES (1) Continuous Contact Printer for picture and sound track. (2) Optical Step Printer for special effects work.

Contact Printers

In continuous contact printers, the negative film and the raw stock to be printed are brought together and exposed as they pass a narrow slit extending across the width of the film. This slit is uniformly illuminated by a lamp, but the intensity of light at the aperture can be accurately adjusted to compensate for variations in the density of the negative from one scene to the next.

Mechanically, the most usual arrangement is to position the slit between the flanges of a large rotating sprocket whose teeth engage the perforation holes of both films. The light from the printing lamp passes between the flanges to illuminate the slit from within and the negative film must therefore be on the inside path so that light passes through it to expose the raw stock on the outside.

To ensure the best contact the spacing between perforation holes on the film wrapped on the inside path should be slightly less than that on the other path. For this reason negative film is usually made with slightly shorter perforation intervals ('short pitch') than positive stock; with a sprocket diameter of 4 inches this difference is usually made to be between 0·2 and 0·3 per cent.

Excellent contact between the two films must, of course, be maintained at the moment of exposure and in addition to the pitch difference and the design of the sprocket tooth form, a pressure roll or shoe is often applied to the films as they pass the aperture.

Sound track printing

The printing of picture and sound track images on continuous printers is substantially similar except for the width of the aperture slit and in release printing machines two exposure positions each with its own sprocket and aperture are often used in tandem on the same machine so that picture and track can be printed successively on the same positive stock at one passage through the machine.

Continuous contact printing machines can be run at high speed, up to several hundred feet a minute. To obtain maximum output in release printing and avoid the delay in rewinding the negative for each print some printers are designed to run both forwards and back so that the negative can be left in position and only a new roll of positive stock fed on to the printing path. Machines of this form often have their picture and sound film paths mounted on separate panels for easy operation and are termed panel printers.

44

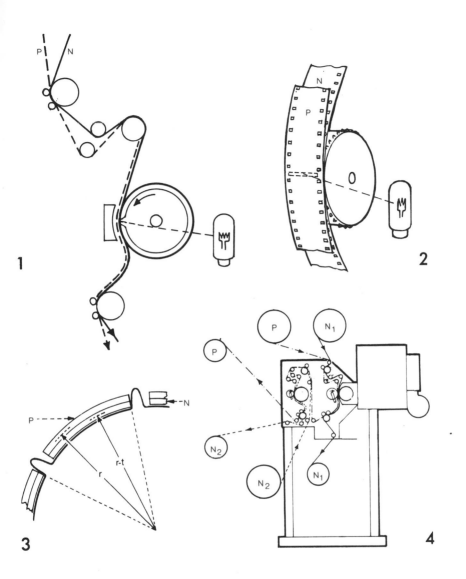

1

2

3

4

CONTACT PRINTERS   The negative film N and the print stock P are brought together in contact (1) and pass over a large rotating sprocket with an illuminated slit at which exposure takes place (2). To maintain good contact, the perforation pitch of the inner negative N should be slightly shorter than the outer positive P in the proportion $(r-t)/r$, where t is the film thickness and r the average radius of the outer layer (3).

In many machines the positive stock P passes two printing positions so that a picture image from negative N_1 and a sound track image from negative N_2 can be exposed at one operation (4).

45

Printer Light Control

All film printers require a means of precisely adjusting the intensity of light at the printing aperture. For black and white this is simple: the brightness of the lamp can be varied by voltage, graded neutral density filters can be inserted or the size of the light beam altered by a variable aperture or light valve. For colour printing, however, both intensity and colour must be controlled.

Two principal systems of colour modulation are now in use, known as subtractive and additive. In the subtractive system, transparent colour filters are inserted in the light beam. By combining a number of these into a 'pack', the required printing light colour can be obtained and neutral density filters added to control intensity.

When a reel of film containing a number of scenes is to be printed a filter pack must be selected and changed for each scene. The filters are inserted in pockets in a transparent carrier strip or attached to a control band with punched diaphragm holes to control the intensity.

The additive system, now general on modern printing machines, uses the controlled mixture of separate red, green and blue light components to produce both the correct intensity and colour. The light from the lamp is divided by reflection and transmission at dichroic filters into separate red, green and blue beams, whose intensities are individually controlled by three light valves. The three components are then brought together again and enter the lens system which illuminates the printing aperture. The operation of the light valves is very rapid, so that the changes from one scene to the next can be made imperceptibly even at high running speeds. The whole sequence of light valve settings for every scene in a reel of film can be coded as holes in a perforated tape and applied automatically during the continuous printing operation.

Exposure steps

The exposure steps used must be small enough to allow very precise variations of colour and intensity to be made. It is now general practice to use steps of 0·025 log E, known as printer points.

For the subtractive system, colour filters are manufactured in series such as 0·025, 0·05, 0·10, 0·20 and 0·40 so that suitable combinations in 0·025 density steps can be selected.

In additive printers, the openings of the light valves are accurately controlled to provide these steps of 0·025 log Exposure units, with a total range of 50 steps from minimum to maximum intensity for each of the three colours. The printing level for any particular negative is specified as the printer point values on this scale for each colour, such as 22 Red, 24 Green, 25 Blue or RGB 22:24:25. Seriously under- or over-exposed negative which cannot be printed within the normal range of printer points from 1 to 50 is termed 'off-scale'.

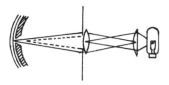

1

2

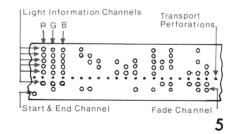

3

PRINTER LIGHT CONTROL The intensity of printing light may be controlled by the size of hole in an opaque control band (1); for subtractive colour correction, transparent gelatine filters may be attached (2).

The opening of a light valve (3) is also used for intensity control. In the additive colour system (4), light from the lamp, d, is divided by dichroic reflectors, a, into separate red, green and blue beams controlled by light valves, b. These beams are re-combined by reflectors, c, to give the required colour and intensity at the printing aperture, d. The settings of the light valve are controlled by a perforated programme tape (5).

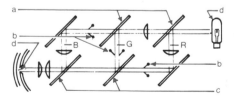

4

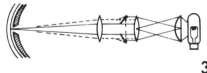

5

47

Step Printers

In a contact step printer the negative film and the positive stock are brought together at the moment of exposure; but instead of the two moving continuously past a slit, they are exposed one picture at a time at an illuminated aperture or gate which is the size of the whole image frame. As in a camera, a rotating shutter must be provided to cut off the light while the films are being moved from one frame to the next.

During the period of exposure, the two films are very accurately positioned in the gate by means of closely fitting register pins which engage a selected pair of perforation holes in each film. In this way it is possible to ensure that the printed image is located in exactly the same place on the film, in relation to the perforations, as the negative image and the location can be accurately repeated in subsequent similar printing operations.

Control of printing light
The illumination of the printing aperture must be as uniform as possible across the frame and a condenser lamphouse system is preferred. With such an arrangement the control of colour by the light valves of an additive system is not easy to apply and contact step printers are frequently used with subtractive filter packs. This is not too much of a disadvantage as their speed of printing is usually comparatively slow.

Step printers are used in all cases where a contact print of utmost steadiness and exact image position is required. Prints for back-projection use in the studio will normally be step printed and separate components such as titles and mattes for special effects must be made this way. One form of protective facilities for colour originals requires printing separate red, green and blue records on three strips of film and this must be done on a step printer to maintain registration of each separate image.

48

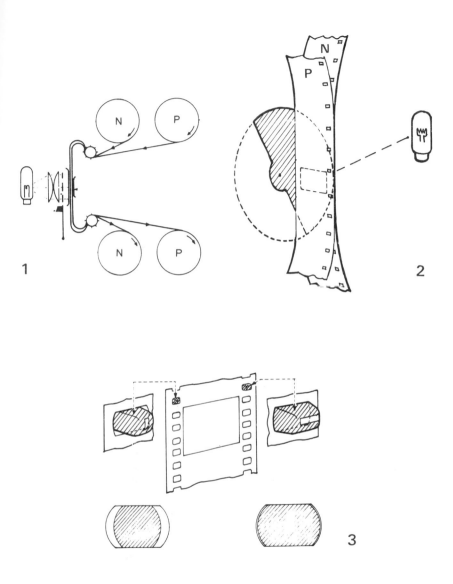

STEP PRINTERS (1) In a contact step printer the negative N and print film P are brought together and exposed one frame at a time. (2) A rotating shutter cuts off the light from the lamp while the films are being moved. (3) To ensure accurate positioning of the two films, 35mm step printers have pairs of register pins one of which fits the perforations exactly on all sides, while the other has small lateral clearance to allow for shrinkage.

Optical Printers

An Optical printer may be regarded as a printing machine combining the characteristics of a projector and a camera, and the film paths of the negative and print stock are sometimes referred to in this way. In the most usual form the negative runs frame by frame through an intermittent mechanism in the projector head where it is illuminated by the optical system of the lamp house. A copying lens forms an image of the negative frame on the emulsion surface of the print film, which is similarly moved frame by frame through the intermittent mechanism of the camera head, a rotating shutter cutting off the light beam while both films move from one frame to the next. Register pin mechanisms are provided in both heads and for special effect work two strips of film can be run simultaneously through either projector or camera (or both).

The two film paths of an optical printer are completely independent and each can run forward or backwards, or stop, without affecting the other. The separation of the heads and the setting of the copy lens can also be adjusted to cover a wide range of magnification or reduction and the two heads can, if necessary, run film of two different gauges and image size.

Light sources
Optical printing normally makes use of very directional (specular) light to illuminate the negative film and this is liable to show up slight scratches and abrasions on the film surface to an objectionable extent. This effect can be greatly reduced by coating the negative with a transparent layer to fill in the abrasions. The coating may either be a permanent lacquer or a suitable volatile liquid, applied at the moment of exposure in what is termed 'wet printing'. In another arrangement, the negative aperture is in the form of a glass-walled cell filled with liquid in which the film is enclosed at the time of exposure; this is known as a 'liquid gate'.

Optical printers differ greatly in their complexity, the simplest forms being those set up permanently for a change of image size, for example, reduction from 35mm to 16mm. In such single function machines no great elaboration is necessary, although a lamp-house providing scene-to-scene colour variations is essential.

Special effects
For special effects work, however, a wide range of functions is necessary and may be controlled by a punched tape computer programme. The camera head will have a dissolving shutter, with reverse and stop motion on both heads. The positions of camera head and copy lens may be automatically focussed and continuously moved to provide zoom effects, and the camera will have a built-in reflex viewer so that the image can be inspected and its location accurately adjusted.

50

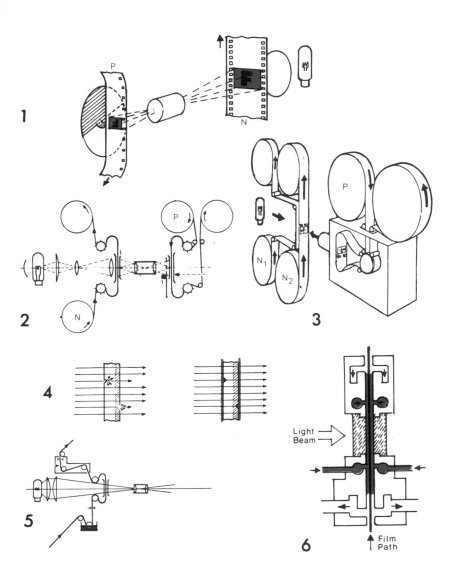

OPTICAL PRINTERS In an optical printer the negative N is imaged by the copying lens on to the print stock P, often with change of size (1); a shutter cuts off the light during the movement from frame to frame. A condenser-relay lamp-house system (2) is used for uniform illumination. In special effects work two strips of negative may run in contact so that both are imaged on the positive in the camera head (3). Optical printing accentuates scratches on the negative surface but these can be reduced by coating the film temporarily with a liquid layer (4). In wet printing (5) the liquid is picked up from a dip tank below the aperture but in the liquid gate (6) the film is enclosed in a glass-walled cell at the moment of exposure.

Continuous Optical Printers

Although optical printing frame by frame on step printers has been an important laboratory operation for many years, the use of continuous optical machines is comparatively recent and has been developed mainly to meet the need for making large numbers of copies by reduction, especially 8mm and Super-8 prints from a 16mm original.

The essential feature of optically printing with continuous film movement is that the speed of the negative film past its exposure slit and the speed of the raw stock must both be uniform and exactly matched in the proportion of the reduction factor of the copy lens. In practice, this is most conveniently achieved by mounting the main sprocket for the negative and the corresponding smaller diameter sprocket for the positive on the same rotating shaft; the path of light through the copy lens system is bent into a U-shape by reflectors to produce an image of the negative aperture slit on the surface of the print film.

Multiple printing

To increase the output of reduction prints from such a machine, the copy lens system may be divided by prisms or additional lenses to produce two or four images of the original side by side on the same strip of positive stock, which is slit after processing to give two or four separate copies. Continuous reduction printers can be operated at high speeds and can be made with forward and reverse running to avoid rewinding the negative between printings. Additive lamphouse systems or filter packs may be used for colour control in printing the picture image.

Some types of Super-8 prints are made with a photographic sound track and an optical reduction system for the picture may be combined on one machine with a contact printing path for the sound, so that combined prints can be made at one passage of the positive stock. A special multi-track sound negative must of course be used to match the multiple images when two or four are simultaneously printed.

52

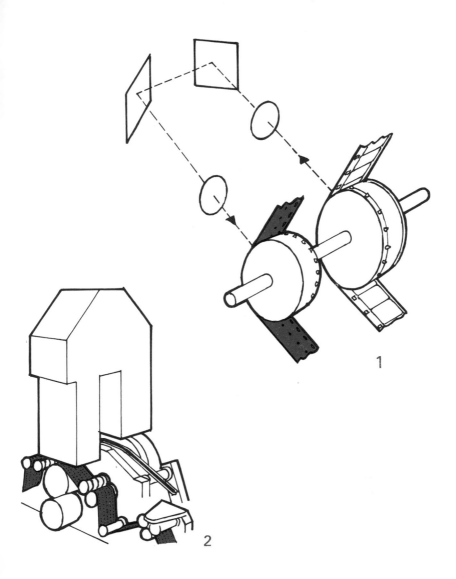

CONTINUOUS OPTICAL PRINTERS   To match the speed of the negative
and print films, they are driven by individual sprockets mounted on the same
shaft (1). The light from the negative through the copy lens system is
returned by reflectors in a U-shaped path to form an image on the positive
stock (2).

53

Positive Processing Equipment

Positive processing machines, being used to develop both rush prints and bulk release prints, are often faster running and of larger output capacity than those used for negatives.

Black and white print processing, like black and white negative, is a simple sequence of Developer/Stop-bath rinse/Fix/Wash/Dry, but colour print stock requires a more complex treatment and the sound track image necessitates an additional process. The need for increased output from machines of limited size has now led to the general use of solution temperatures of 80°F (30°C) rather than the earlier 70° or 75°C, which allows an increase of running speed of the order of 30 to 40 per cent.

Colour print stocks usually have an anti-halation backing and this must first be softened in a pre-bath and then washed off. Colour development then takes about $5\frac{1}{2}$ minutes at 80°F, after which the film is given a spray wash and enters the first fixing solution. Another wash precedes the bleaching stage which converts the developed silver image back to silver halide and a wash then removes bleach chemicals.

Sound track striping

The silver halides may then be removed to leave the coloured dye image, but such a dye image is not suitable for sound track reproduction. The photocells normally used in cinema projector sound heads are sensitive mainly to deep red and infra-red radiation and colour dye images are substantially transparent to these rays. The silver halides of the image in the sound track area only are turned back into metallic silver by applying a narrow stripe of viscous developer solution to this area. It is usual to divert the film, from the main series of machine racks, to apply the track developer and the subsequent spray wash and feed it back into the normal sequence at the second fix tank.

It should be noted that track striping is not used for Super-8 prints with photographic sound since the photo-cells on Super-8 projectors are suitably sensitive to use dye images.

After fixing, the positive is washed at length, given its final stabilising treatment and dried. With solutions at 80°F the wet processing time is 20 minutes and the total including drying, about 28 minutes. A further reduction can be achieved by using a hypo-eliminator solution to shorten final wash time.

Colour reversal print materials are generally processed in the same way as reversal originals, with the appropriate alterations to the first and colour developers. Sound track striping is also necessary for this type of stock, producing either a silver sound track image, or in the case of some materials a silver sulphide image.

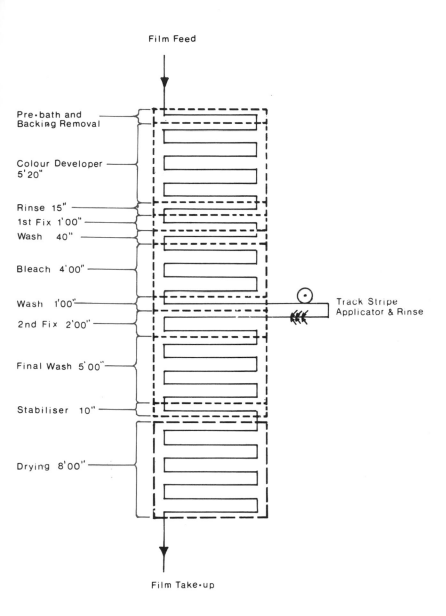

Film Feed

Pre·bath and Backing Removal

Colour Developer 5'20"

Rinse 15"
1st Fix 1'00"
Wash 40"

Bleach 4'00"

Wash 1'00"

2nd Fix 2'00"

Track Stripe Applicator & Rinse

Final Wash 5'00"

Stabiliser 10"

Drying 8'00"

Film Take·up

COLOUR POSITIVE PROCESSING SEQUENCE A temperature of 80°F (30°C) is often used to allow higher running speeds. This machine with 23 solution tank racks of up to 100 feet each and 7 drying racks has a capacity of 6000 feet per hour with a total processing time of 28 minutes at a speed of 100 feet per minute.

General Film Handling Equipment 1

While processing and printing machines are the largest and most specialised groups for laboratory use, a very wide range of general film handling equipment is also involved, especially for negative preparation. The essential units are inspection tables with rewinds and tight-winds, film measurers and synchronisers, and film joiners or splicing machines.

Inspection tables and cutting tables are usually fitted with illuminated panels or light boxes in their surfaces, so that the film can be examined by the transmitted light. Geared rewinders to allow the film to be wound across the light box are fitted on each side, with the rolls of film either horizontally or vertically. Rewinds with horizontal flat plates supporting the roll are often used to handle film wound on small plastic cores (bobbins) but the vertical form is more convenient with film on metal or plastic sided spools. Film on cores is however often handled with vertical rewinds, either on split reels with removable flanges, on single-flanged plates or on spindles with tight-wind rollers. Film on cores can also be carried on an open frame called a "horse" on the feed position of an inspection table (usually the left hand side) but cannot then be wound up on this side.

Measuring equipment
Film measurers or counters are large sprockets, usually marked with frame intervals round the circumference, and connected to a re-settable revolution counter. For 35mm work the sprocket has 64 or 32 teeth, corresponding to 16 or 8 frames, 1 or $\frac{1}{2}$ foot, while for 16mm film, sprockets with 40 or 20 frames are used.

Synchronisers
Synchronisers allow several strips of film to be wound through together exactly in step. They consist of two, four or six sprockets mounted on the same shaft, sometimes with clutches between them to allow one to be rotated independently of the others, or locked together as required. Some synchronisers for laboratory use are fitted with pairs of different sprockets, say 35 and 16mm, so that films of two different gauges can be matched frame by frame.

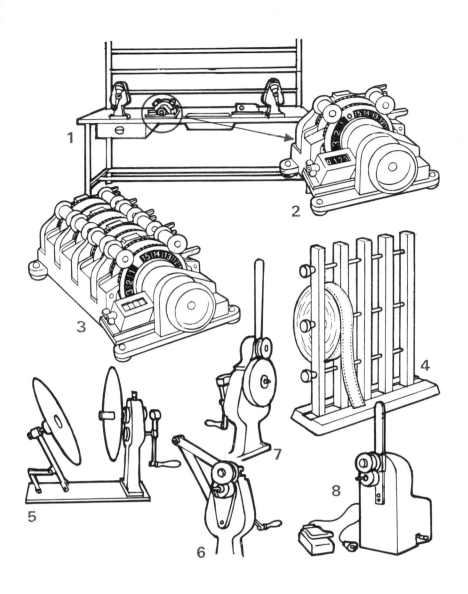

GENERAL FILM HANDLING EQUIPMENT 1   (1) Rewind Bench for
inspection or cutting with illuminated panel and spool trays. (2) Film measurer
for 35mm film. (3) Synchroniser for four strips of 35mm. (4) Four-way Horse
for rolls of film on cores. (5) Plate re-wind for film on core, with removable
safety plate. (6) & (7) Rewind with tight-wind followers. (8) Motorised tight-
wind with foot switch control.

General Film Handling Equipment 2

The splicing machines used in laboratory operations are always those making a cemented join and the adhesive tape joins generally employed by editors in the studio cutting room are not used. It is important to realise that laboratory splices are expected to stand up to protracted use, either in printing or on projection, and must therefore be accurately cut and aligned, the emulsion layer scraped off to the correct depth and fresh cement used to ensure a strong weld. Even the simplest hand-splicers should be fitted with semi-automatic scrapers to remove the emulsion and those machines with precise settings for cut width, thickness and pressure, together with heated blocks to hasten setting, are preferable.

Width of splices
The strength of a cemented splice naturally depends to a considerable extent on the width of the overlap and different widths are used for different purposes. Joins in the negative occur at every scene change and must therefore be invisible but a wider splice in a positive print, perhaps only once in a reel, can be accepted. An overlap of one full perforation hole can be very strong but encroaches to an appreciable extent into the picture image area, so that it is normally only used exceptionally, even on positive prints. The maximum inter-perforation splice on 35mm is approximately 0·080" wide (2·03mm) and this is generally used for positive films; a narrower splice 0·050" wide (1·27mm) is desirable in negatives to clear the picture area and for cinemascope negatives an overlap as small as 0·030" (0·75mm) may be necessary. In 16mm even the narrowest half-hole overlap of 0·070" (1·78mm) is very visible in the picture area and special cutting and printing techniques are necessary to eliminate their appearance on the screen in the resultant print.

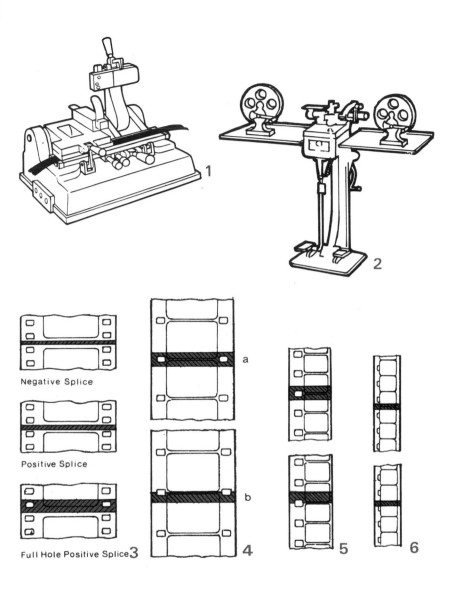

Negative Splice

Positive Splice

Full Hole Positive Splice 3

a

b

4

5

6

GENERAL FILM HANDLING EQUIPMENT 2   (1) Cement splicer for use on rewind bench. (2) Foot-operated Pedestal Splicer with its own rewinds. (3) 35mm cemented splices, for negative and print. (4) 16mm cemented splices, (a) full hole overlap, (b) half-hole overlap. (5) Regular 8mm cemented splices, for prints only. (6) Super-8 cemented splices, for prints only.

Negative Identification & Packing

The first laboratory service to be required by a production company is the processing of their exposed original material and for this the film unloaded from the camera must be identified and delivered to or collected by the laboratory together with the necessary instructions for the work required.

Essential identification for every roll of film must show that it is EXPOSED film for processing and in addition:—

Type of Material (Colour or B & W, Negative, Reversal, etc.)
Emulsion Number
Film Gauge, 35 or 16mm
(All these specify the type of processing machine required)
The Customer or Production Company and the subject title or reference.
The approximate length of the roll and . . .
Any special instructions (Forced Development, Test Sections, etc.).

Many laboratories supply printed labels to be filled in for such identification, often colour coded for easy recognition of different materials; some production companies, however, prefer to use their own labels; in which case the laboratory chosen for the work must be shown.

Care of film
Film for processing must be sent to the laboratory in good condition. Considering that a single roll of exposed negative may be the only product from the work of hundreds of people at the cost of thousands of pounds, it is amazing how often this point is forgotten. The film unloaded from the camera magazine should be reasonably tightly wound, on plastic core or similar centre, and with the outside end taped down. Even if the film is sent on a daylight loading spool the end should be taped to prevent unwinding. Loose rolls are a real source of damage from scratches, dirt and abrasions. The roll should be wrapped in a clean black paper bag, such as those used by the raw stock manufacturer, and packed in a can which is then sealed with adhesive tape *around the edge*. This is a well-recognised indication that the contents are EXPOSED UNDEVELOPED and that the can must only be opened in a photographic dark room.

Film for processing should not be scribed, notched or punched as such markings cause points of weakness which might break on the developing machine. A warning of any possible broken perforations found on camera checks between scenes should be noted on the can, so that the film may be given special examination before processing. The ends of rolls are often found to have bent edges or nicks as a result of careless handling in loading or unloading and important action may be lost if these portions have to be removed before developing.

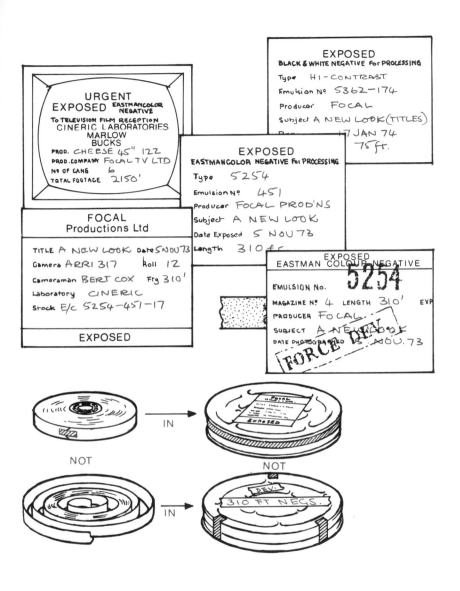

NEGATIVE IDENTIFICATION AND PACKING Exposed Negative or other original material sent for processing must be clearly identified; the film should be wound on a plastic core and the end taped down. The can should be labelled and sealed with tape around its edge for safety.

Protection in Transit

After exposure, film should not be kept in the camera magazine any longer than necessary and after unloading it should be sent to the laboratory as quickly as possible. When working at a studio or location near the processing plant, this presents no problems, but on more distant sites precautions may be necessary.

High temperature and humidity can affect the latent image in the exposed film and the results on colour materials can be serious. Packages of unloaded film can get sufficiently hot to cause damage if they are left in the sun to await transport. If long delays are expected, refrigerated cool storage is recommended.

On the other hand excessive cold can cause the film to become brittle, particularly if it becomes very dry. This can happen not only in arctic conditions, but also during high altitude air transport if the film is carried in an uncontrolled baggage compartment. Sealing the edge of the can by adhesive tape helps to slow down the loss of moisture from the roll for a limited time.

Air freight

Another hazard of international air freight is the possibility of fogging caused by radio-active substances; the proximity of normally safe isotopes can cause serious penetration of the roll of film in a few hours and the light-weight metal can offers only negligible protection. Boxes of exposed motion picture film, like all sensitive photographic material, should be boldly labelled with a warning to keep well away from any radioactive materials whatsoever. It is advisable to have such labels worded in several different languages when working abroad.

EXPOSED EASTMANCOLOR NEGATIVE

DELIVER URGENTLY TO

CENTRAL FILM RECEPTION

CINERIC LABORATORIES
MARLOW
BUCKS

PROD. "A NEW LOOK"

PROD. COMPANY FOCAL

No. OF CANS 4

TOTAL FOOTAGE 1350

ST. 148

UNDEVELOPED FILM

MANUFACTURED BY EASTMAN KODAK COMPANY

PROTECT FROM

RADIOACTIVE MATERIALS

EO 3449 KP 63994A

Kodak

MOTION PICTURE NEGATIVE

MUST BE CONSIGNED IN CABIN

CONTENTS WILL BE DAMAGED BY TEMPERATURE
VARIATIONS AS IN FREIGHT COMPARTMENT

PROTECT FROM RADIUM AND **X-RAYS**
AND ALL **RADIO-ACTIVE SUBSTANCES**
AVER CURA

PER FAVORE PROTEGGETE CONTRO RADIUM RAGGI ROENTZEN
ET CALORE PER FAVORE MANEGGIATE AVER CURA

OPEN ONLY IN TOTAL DARKNESS

OUVRIR EN OBSCURITÉ COMPLÈTE SEULEMENT ABRASE UNICAMENTE EN COMPLETA OBSCURIDAD
DARF NUR IN EINEM VOLLKOMMEN VERDENKELTEN RAUM GEÖFFNET WERDEN
AYRIRE SOLO NEL BUIO PIU COMPLETO

MOTION PICTURE NEGATIVE

PROTECTION IN TRANSIT   Batches of exposed negative being sent for processing should be labelled with warnings to keep away from radio-active materials and to open only in a dark room.

Camera Reports

Instructions to the laboratory for printing the processed camera originals are generally supplied in the form of picture negative report sheets or camera logs on which details of the day's photography are entered by a member of the camera crew in accordance with the director's wishes. There are several types of these reports in regular use but an essential feature of all of them is the indication of which scenes and takes on the negative are to be printed, either in colour or black and white, together with the length of the shot and any special information as to the character of the lighting and other effects which might help the grader.

Film Producers Association report form
The well-known report form devised for the Film Producers Association sets out the take numbers of each scene vertically with a separate line for each and separate columns to indicate B and W or Colour printing and this arrangement is clear and unambiguous. As will be seen later, it is very easy to follow this lay-out when breaking down the negative for printing, after processing, and it is therefore popular with the laboratory staff.

Other report forms
Other types of picture negative report use one line only for the slate number of each scene and set out columns for the individual takes horizontally. In each of these the length of each take is to be entered and those to be printed marked in accordance with the convention used for the particular report sheet. Unfortunately these conventions have not been standardised and the camera assistant completing the log must be very careful to use the correct system for the particular form. For example, some sheets state 'Print Circled Takes only', while others use a circled take number for printing on black and white and a square boxed take for colour. In another type it is the circled takes which are NOT to be printed, which can be most confusing. In general, report sheets with this horizontal sequence of take numbers are more compact and several rolls of negative can be covered by a single sheet, but their subsequent interpretation in the laboratory is not quite as straightforward as when using the FPA type.

All types of reports have, however, the joint purpose of providing the laboratory with instructions for work and the production company with a record of photography completed. The report is a formal order to the laboratory with its appropriate reference number and at the same time an indication to the editor and cutting room staff what rush prints are to be supplied as a result of those operations. Copies are therefore sent to the Cutting Rooms, the Production Office and Accounts Department as well as to the laboratory, with a copy retained by the Camera Department.

LABORATORIES COPY   Nº 3751

CONTINUED FROM SHEET Nº	SHEET NUMBER	CONTINUED ON SHEET Nº

THE SHEET NUMBERS MUST BE QUOTED ON ALL DELIVERY NOTES, INVOICES, AND OTHER COMMUNICATIONS RELATING THERETO

PRODUCING COMPANY	STUDIOS OR LOCATION
PRODUCTION	PRODUCTION No.

DIRECTOR	CAMERAMAN	DATE

STATE IF COLOUR OR B&W

PICTURE NEGATIVE REPORT

ORDER TO	LABORATORIES
STOCK AND CODE Nº	LABORATORY INSTRUCTIONS RE INVOICING, DELIVERY, ETC.	CAMERA AND NUMBER
EMULSION AND ROLL Nº		CAMERA OPERATOR

MAG. No.	LENGTH LOADED	SLATE No.	TAKE Nº	COUNTER READING	TAKE LENGTH	'P' FOR PRINT B&W	COL'R	LENS F/L & STOP	ESSENTIAL INFORMATION ★ SEE REQUIREMENTS BELOW	CAN No.

FOR OFFICE USE ONLY | TOTAL CANS |

TOTAL EXPOSED	TOTAL EXPOSED	TOTAL PRINTED	TOTAL FOOTAGE PREVIOUSLY DRAWN	
SHORT ENDS	HELD OR NOT SENT	B&W	FOOTAGE DRAWN TODAY	
WASTE	TOTAL DEVELOPED	COLOUR	PREVIOUSLY EXPOSED	
FOOTAGE LOADED			EXPOSED TODAY	

SIGNED : _____

★ COLOUR DESCRIPTION OF SCENE, FILTER AND/OR DIFFUSION USED DAY, NIGHT OR OTHER EFFECTS
DAYLIGHT, ARCS, INKIES OR MIXED LIGHTING.   INTERIOR/EXTERIOR A.M., P.M.

PRODUCTION COMPANY	NO. 4808
DATE	PRODUCTION
CAMERAMAN	DIRECTOR
LABORATORY	EMULSION DETAILS

MUTE NEGATIVE REPORT

SLATE Nº	TAKES 1 2 3 4 5 6 7 8	REMARKS	TOT

○ PRINT BLACK AND WHITE
☐ PRINT COLOUR

Do not print circled takes

PRODUCTION	
CAMERAMAN	DIRECTOR
ROLL Nº	

PRINT CIRCLED TAKES ONLY

SCENE	TAKE	FOOTAGE	REMARKS

Mag. Nº	Roll Nº	Slate Nº	1	2	3	4	5	6	7	TOTAL Nº PER SLATE	TOTAL PRINT PER SLATE	REMARKS

PRINT CIRCLED TAKES ONLY	TOTALS:		WASTE
TOTAL FOR LABORATORIES THIS SHEET:			TOTAL USED
LABORATORY INSTRUCTIONS			

CAMERA REPORTS   Camera report sheets of several different types may be found in use but all have the purpose of recording the course of production photography and instructing the laboratory of the rush prints required. Note that different conventions are sometimes used to indicate the scenes and takes which are to be printed.

Camera Report Details

All the detailed information entered on the picture negative report is of importance at one stage or another.

The type of negative stock used and details of the emulsion and roll number are needed by the laboratory in setting processing and printing conditions and the camera number may be useful if defects in photography have to be traced.

Essential details

The details of each slated scene and take number are vital for selecting those portions of the negative for printing after processing. At the end of each take, the camera footage counter is read so that the approximate length of the shot can be noted for comparison with the actual film. Some camera counters count down from the length of the roll originally loaded, as is shown in this example, while others start at zero and show the increasing length of film run during the sequence of takes. Printing instructions for each take must be indicated for colour or black and white. Some directors like to subdivide the unprinted take into 'NG', completely unsatisfactory, and 'hold takes', which might possibly be required for printing if those originally selected are defective in any way. In the absence of other information, the laboratory will store all unprinted takes as 'second negative'. The total footages for film to be developed and printed allow the laboratory to make a quick check against their own records that nothing has been inadvertently missed.

Other information

The details of the focal length of the lens used and its stop setting are not essential but can be helpful in grading the negative and reporting to the cameraman. Lenses can differ in their colour characteristics and the bias given by a particular lens can be recognised and corrected for in advance.

Information as to the colour character of the scene photographed should be given to help the rush print grader wherever possible, especially where an unusual lighting effect is being applied. 'Day or night', 'exterior or interior', are basic essentials and characteristics such as 'Dawn', 'Dusk', 'Firelight', 'Candlelight', 'Moonlight' must be noted, as also the frequently used 'Day for Night' style. Similarly, the laboratory should be warned of any camera effect which might possibly be interpreted as a fault: the use of diffusion during photography might otherwise be reported 'out of focus' and an intentional firelight flicker thought to be irregular exposure.

The history of the scenes and takes covered by the camera log sheet shown here will now be followed through their subsequent stages of negative preparation, rush printing and reporting.

66

CUTTING ROOMS COPY   No 3751

ACCOUNTS DEPARTMENT COPY   No 3751

PRODUCTION OFFICE COPY   No 3751

CAMERA DEPARTMENT COPY   No 3751

LABORATORIES COPY   No 3751

CONTINUED FROM SHEET Nº	SHEET NUMBER 1	CONTINUED ON SHEET Nº

THE SHEET NUMBERS MUST BE QUOTED ON ALL DELIVERY NOTES, INVOICES, AND OTHER COMMUNICATIONS RELATING THERETO.

PRODUCING COMPANY	FOCAL PROD'NS	STUDIOS OR LOCATION	HENSHAW
PRODUCTION	'A NEWLOOK'	PRODUCTION No.	735

DIRECTOR ALBERT BOX   CAMERAMAN BERT COX   DATE 5. NOV. 73

STATE IF COLOUR OR B&W COLOUR

PICTURE NEGATIVE REPORT

ORDER TO   CINERIC   LABORATORIES

STOCK AND CODE Nº	LABORATORY INSTRUCTIONS RE INVOICING, DELIVERY, ETC.	CAMERA AND NUMBER
E/C 5254	FOCAL CUTTING ROOMS	ARRI 317
EMULSION AND ROLL Nº	HENSHAW STUDIOS	CAMERA OPERATOR
451-17	BUCKS.	J. DOE.

MAG. No.	LENGTH LOADED	SLATE No.	TAKE Nº	COUNTER READING	TAKE LENGTH	F FOR PRINT B&W	COL'R	LENS F/L & STOP	ESSENTIAL INFORMATION ★ SEE REQUIREMENTS BELOW	CAN No.
2	400'	207	1	380	20		/	50"/M	4.0 ALL NIGHT INT.	12
			2	345	35	P			FIRELIGHT.	
			3	315	30	P				
		208	1	300	15		/	50"/M	4.0	
			2	280	20	P				
		209	1	270	10		/	75"/M		
			2	255	15		/			
			3	220	35	P				
		210	1	180	40	P		75"/M	3.5	
		211	1	150	30		/	35"/M	3.5 ⎫ FIRELIGHT	
			2	120	30	P			⎬ FLICKER	
			3	90	30	P			⎭ EFFECT	

			FOR OFFICE USE ONLY	TOTAL CANS	I
TOTAL EXPOSED	310'	TOTAL EXPOSED 310'	TOTAL PRINTED	TOTAL FOOTAGE PEVIOUSLY DRAWN	
SHORT ENDS	90'	HELD OR NOT SENT 90'	B&W, 60	FOOTAGE DRAWN TODAY	
WASTE		TOTAL DEVELOPED 310'	COLOUR, 160	PREVIOUSLY EXPOSED	
FOOTAGE LOADED	400'			EXPOSED TODAY	

SIGNED : J. Doe.

★ COLOUR DESCRIPTION OF SCENE. FILTER AND/OR DIFFUSION USED DAY, NIGHT OR OTHER EFFECTS. DAYLIGHT, ARCS, INKIES OR MIXED LIGHTING.   INTERIOR/EXTERIOR A.M., P.M.

CAMERA REPORT DETAILS An example of a completed picture negative report with all details entered. Carbon copies are sent to the Editor in the Cutting Rooms and to other departments of the Production Company for their records.

Negative Break-Down & Make-Up

After processing, all the scenes and takes exposed on a particular roll of negative must be sub-divided for printing according to the instructions given on the camera log; this is termed the 'break-down' of the roll and the joining of the selected sections is termed 'make-up'. When the negative is received for processing, it is allocated a laboratory roll number by which it is identified and recorded at all later stages; if some takes are to be printed as colour rush prints and others as black and white, two separate roll numbers may be used or the same number with 'A' and 'B' or '−1' and '−2' part suffixes.

The negative break-down operator winds the developed negative through a film measurer or footage counter, identifying each scene and take against the camera report by the image of the slate board photographed at the head end, and verifying the length of each section measured against the log to make sure that no information has been missed or incorrectly recorded. At this stage he will also make a note of the stock edge numbers and their sequence throughout the roll for future reference.

Make-up into rolls

Scenes and takes not specified for printing on the camera log will be wound together at this stage as the 'second negative', usually without splicing together, but the scenes to be printed are joined in sequence in one or more rolls in preparation for printing, and given their roll number identification.

As the scenes in the roll are joined, the make-up operator notches the edge of the film at each splice so that the light change mechanism of the printing machine will be actuated to set the required printing exposure level for each scene. The actual point at which the light value is changed is usually a number of frames, often 6 or 8, beyond the position of the notch and this means that the alteration in printing level takes place just after the start of the new scene, generally during the slate at the beginning of the take.

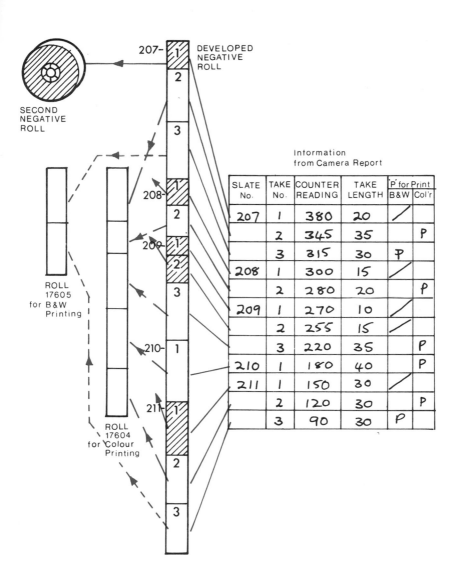

Information from Camera Report

SLATE No.	TAKE No.	COUNTER READING	TAKE LENGTH	P for Print B&W	Print Col'r
207	1	380	20	/	
	2	345	35		P
	3	315	30	P	
208	1	300	15	/	
	2	280	20		P
209	1	270	10	/	
	2	255	15	/	
	3	220	35		P
210	1	180	40		P
211	1	150	30	/	
	2	120	30		P
	3	90	30	P	

NEGATIVE BREAKDOWN After the negative has been developed it is divided according to camera report instructions into scenes for colour or black-and-white printing and these are spliced together. Unprinted material (Second Negative) is spooled separately.

Rush Print Grading (1)

Once the scenes of negative selected for printing have been assembled in their rolls, the next operation is to determine the exposure level (in printer points) to be used on the printing machine to give a satisfactory result. This is known in Britain as grading and in the United States as timing or lighting.

Black-and-white rushes

A suitable printer point for printing acceptable black and white rushes from colour originals can usually be estimated visually by an experienced operator. However, as blue-sensitive stock is normally used for rush prints, the tonal rendering of coloured objects in the subject is often rather distorted. Black and white prints are thus suitable only for checking the action, and should not be used to judge colour photographic quality.

Colour rushes

The visual grading of colour negatives is difficult, even with much experience. The operator therefore needs to be assisted, either by some form of photographic test or by closed circuit colour television equipment. In all cases, of course, any special characteristics required by the lighting director and indicated on the camera report sheet must be taken into account.

Photographic tests must provide the necessary information with the minimum use of expensive colour film stock. In a number of laboratories, particularly in Europe, it is the practice to cut a two-frame clipping of negative from the very end of each take to be printed. These clippings are spliced together and printed at an estimated printer point value. The resulting short print is examined by the grader after developing and the necessary corrections estimated visually for each scene and take. There are disadvantages: the preparation of the clipping roll involves extra work and the frames available at the end of the take may not represent the scene as a whole. An alternative system allows a number of test frames to be printed from any section of the assembled roll.

The Scene Tester is a special form of printing machine on which a short portion of the uncut negative, 8 or 12 frames in length, is laid along the circumference of a semi-circular drum which can be illuminated from within. A similar length of colour print stock is laid in contact on the outside and exposed through the negative. A series of neutral density and colour filters mounted within the drum ensure that each frame of the series is printed with slight differences in colour and density, which helps estimation of the corrections required. Many cameramen like to examine these grading strips, sometimes called colour pilots.

For black and white productions, similar test strips (termed Cinex strips) are used to show the effect of printing at various levels.

70

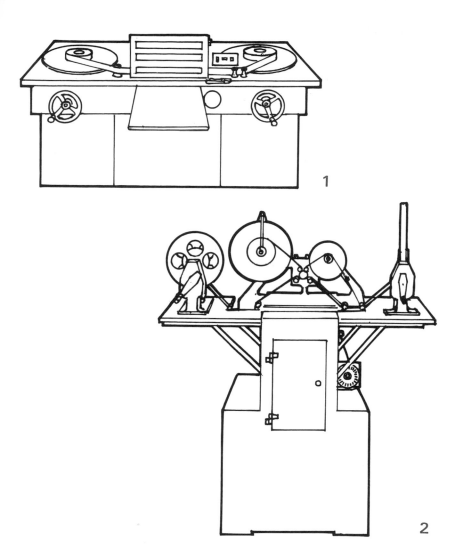

1

2

RUSH PRINT GRADING (1)　(1) Grading inspection table with flat rewinds
allowing the negative to be compared with reference strips against a light-box
panel. (2) Scene Tester which allows short sections of the negative a few frames
in length to be printed with slight differences in colour and density in each
frame.

Rush Print Grading (2)

Although photographic test print methods can provide an accurate basis for making the full length rush print, they are time consuming, and can cause unacceptable delays. It is possible to eliminate both the cost of printing and processing test sections and the time involved by the use of electronic colour analysers.

These are essentially closed circuit colour television systems in which a frame of negative is scanned by a flying spot beam and electronically converted to display a colour positive image on a television monitor screen. Separate controls allow the gain on the red, green and blue channels of the system to be individually adjusted in calibrated steps until the result on the monitor is judged satisfactory. The values selected for each scene and take of negative can be read off and used to set the light valves on an additive-head printer when making the photographic print of the roll. With additional equipment, the selected settings can be transferred directly on the punched paper strip which controls the printer light valves.

One-light printing

However carried out, all grading operations cost money and take time. Of course, if every factor could be kept constant—the photographic sensitivity of the negative stock, the cameraman's lighting and exposure and the development process—rush print grading would be unnecessary and every scene on every day's work could be printed at the same level. A number of laboratories now offer a cheaper rush print service based on this concept and termed 'one-light rushes'. For this, a standard printer point level for all rushes is established with the cameraman with reference to the first day's photography. Sometimes by agreement between the laboratory and cameraman the strict 'one-light' setting may be modified by a standard factor for certain lighting effects specified on the camera report sheet for separate rolls. For example, all scenes noted as 'night interior' might be printed 3 points heavier and 2 points more blue than the standard level.

Successful use of 'one-light' colour rush prints demands consistent exposure by the lighting director and camera operator. It is, however, unlikely to be disturbed by variation in emulsion sensitivity (within one batch) or by processing variations. When working in a studio with all lighting under control, excellent one-light results can be obtained, although uniform exposure presents more problems on exterior locations.

Whatever grading system is used, the information must be used to control the light valves of the printer lamp house. This is usually done with a punched tape, having coded holes for each light value of red, green and blue; but for one-light rushes the light valves may be set manually.

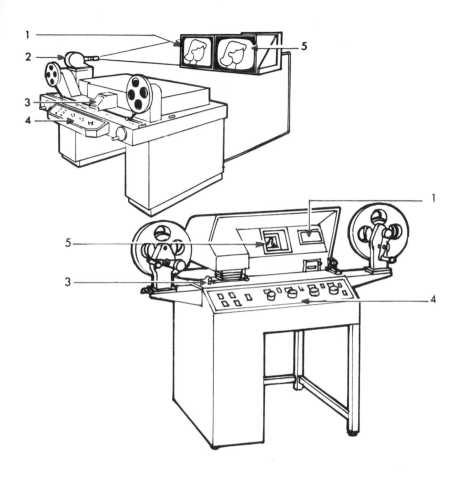

RUSH PRINT GRADING (2)   Two types of electronic colour analysers : in each the negative is wound through the scanning head (3) from which a closed circuit colour TV system produces a positive image on the monitor screen (5). The colour and density of picture can be adjusted by controls (4) calibrated in printer points. A reference picture (1) can be projected from a film clipping by a still projector (2).

73

Rush Printing Records

However the grading is done, the results must be recorded for the cameraman and for subsequent use by the laboratory. Each assembled roll of negative for rush printing therefore has a printer record sheet or card, although for one-light rushes a single card giving the standard settings will be used for a large number of rolls.

Additive printers

The printing values are given as the settings of the three light valves, normally on a scale of 0 to 50. The sequence of colours is likely to be red-green-blue (R-G-B) but B-G-R and B-R-G may be found; these terms refer to the colour of light component in the printer, not to the effect on the print. In negative/positive work, each light component controls the amount of the complementary hue in the print: thus increasing the printer point value for B will make the print more yellow while decreasing it will make it less yellow, so that it will appear lighter and bluer. For this reason some laboratories record their printer data in terms of the complementary effect in the print; thus, the printer lights B-G-R may be shown as Y-M-C, yellow-magenta-cyan. For colour positives from colour negatives the effects are:

Printer Light Change		Effect on Print
+B	:	more yellow
−B	:	less yellow (lighter and bluer)
+G	:	more magenta (reddish-purple)
−G	:	less magenta (lighter and greener)
+R	:	more Cyan (blue-green)
−R	:	less Cyan (lighter and redder)
+BG	:	more red
+GR	:	more blue
+RB	:	more green
+BGR	:	heavier in all colours, i.e. darker
−BGR	:	lighter in all colours.

When additive lamp systems are used in making reversal prints the results are the opposite. For example, increasing the blue printing light will decrease the amount of the yellow image produced, so that the print will appear lighter and more blue.

Subtractive printers

The records are usually a number representing the intensity level, often on a 21 or 24 point scale, and the filter pack. Thus 12, 10R 05M would indicate a light level of 12 with a pack of a red filter of density 0·10 and a magenta one of 0·05. Corrections by filter pack change by subtracting the colour of the filter added; thus increasing the Magenta, say from 05M to 15M, will decrease the magenta component in the print, which will therefore appear lighter and greener.

74

Form 1: PRINTER SHEET

CUST REF 375I   **PRINTER SHEET**

Date of Photog: 5.NOV.73
Date of Report: 5.NOV.73
Company. FOCAL
Cameraman COX
Consignment No 12
Neg. Charged 310 fr
Neg. Emulsion. 5254-457-17

ROLL No 17604 COL
PRODUCTION 'A NEW LOOK'
. Type of Photog: WIDE-SCREEN

Stock Edge No
START: E2X 0993457
END: E2X 0993765

Date Made-up 6·11·73   M/U Opr. 242
Total Neg.Ftge. 310   MU footage 160 COL

PRINTING INSTRUCTIONS

LIGHTING Tech and Effect	Scene & Take	Scene Edge Nos. Start	Finish	PRINTER DATA R | G | B	R | G | B	CORR'N
NIGHT INT.	207-2	478	512	20 | 28 | 26	| |	
FIRELIGHT	208-2	557	576	20 | 28 | 26	| |	
	209-3	603	637	21 | 30 | 28	| |	-1R
	210-1	638	676	21 | 30 | 28	| |	-1R
(FLICKER	211-2	707	738	21 | 30 | 28	| |	
EFFECT)				| |	| |	

Form 2: PRINTER SHEET PICTURE NEGATIVE

2

PRINTER SHEET
PICTURE NEGATIVE   No. 26207

PRODUCTION 'A NEW LOOK'   PRODUCER FOCAL
CAMERAMAN COX   STOCK E/C 451-17   CAMERA RPT. No 3751   DATE 5.NOV

ROLL	SLATE	Take	Y	M	C	REMARKS	ROLL	SLATE	Take	Y	M	C	REMARKS
604	207	2	26	28	20	Firelight Flicker							
	208	2	26	28	20	"							
	209	3	27	29	21	" "							
	210	1	27	29	21	" "							
	21	2											

Form 3: ONE-LIGHT TECHNIQUE CARD

ONE-LIGHT TECHNIQUE CARD
Production 'A NEW LOOK'   Cameraman COX

INTERIOR 30.24.20. Date	Roll No	DAY EXT. 26.24.21. Date	Roll No	NITE EXT. 32.27.24 Date	Roll No
29 Oct	15812	1 Nov	16422	2 Nov	16816
30 Oct	15947	"	16423	"	16817
31 Oct	16003	2 Nov	16815		
5 Nov	17604				
"	17605				
6 Nov	17711				

RUSH PRINTING RECORDS In some systems the Printer information is entered on a copy of the Breakdown Sheet (1) but in other cases a new form is prepared which also serves as the Viewing Report (2). Where one-light rush prints are supplied the agreed printing levels are noted on a record card on which the negative roll numbers are entered (3).

Exposure Rating

The negative report to the studio is an important link between the production company and the laboratory. Very often the cameraman will call the rushes department at the laboratory first thing in the morning for a verbal report on the results of his work on the previous day. Such initial reports are normally supplemented by a more detailed report giving scene-by-scene rating of the negatives' printing levels. Some laboratories report the actual three colour printer point values for each scene, but others often quote either an average level or the R or G printer point only as an indication of the negative exposure rating. The cameraman should find out from his laboratory contact the basis used for their reports and the printer point level chosen to indicate the middle of the scale, which may range from 24 to 27 in different organisations.

Acceptable exposure variations
With a printer point increment of 0·025 log E the theoretical correction for one camera stop would be 8 points on the printer scale. If the printer points reported generally lie between 20 and 30, the exposure will be within ± ½ a stop of optimum, but ratings consistently lower than 18 or higher than 36 call for a correction of lighting or diaphragm. With reversal originals, the latitude permissible is less than that on negatives, so the printer point rating should be between 24 and 32 for best results.

When one-light rushes are supplied, the effect of quite small exposure variations will be obvious. The contact man will advise the cameraman of scenes which fall outside the normally acceptable range of corrections.

Effects of exposure on image quality
The image quality loss from serious exposure errors should be clearly recognised: one-light prints from badly underexposed negative will look very dark and heavy overall and when corrected to make the high-light areas sufficiently bright, the shadows will be thin and washed-out with too little tonal gradation and often a marked colour cast. This tendency will be particularly objectionable in low key scenes and night effect shots.

One light prints from over-exposed negative on the other hand will appear much too light with bare and burnt-out high-lights.

Somewhat similar characteristics can be seen on original reversal materials with over- and under-exposure, and in addition under-exposure is liable to give an image of apparently high contrast with marked differences in colour balance from light to dark tones. Over-exposure on the other hand will tend to give rather flat pictures even when printing corrections have been made. It is practically impossible to compensate for contrast variations when printing from seriously over- or under-exposed materials.

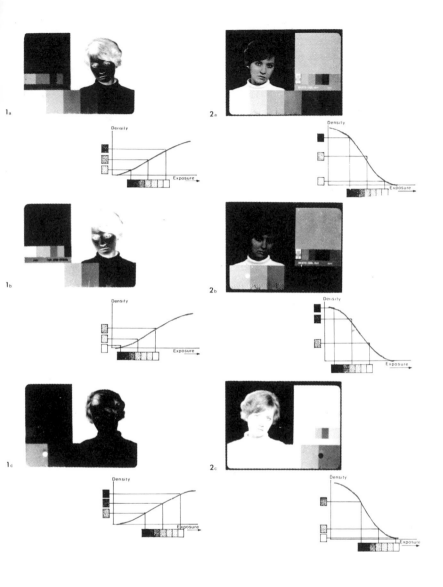

EXPOSURE VARIATIONS   The relation between subject brightness and density of the processed film can be represented by an S-shaped curve. Correct exposure (1a for Negative, 2a for Reversal) gives good tonal distribution along the straight part of this curve. Under-exposed negative (1b) is too thin with shadow tones poorly differentiated, while over-exposed negative (1c) is too heavy to print satisfactorily. In reversal, under-exposure (2b) is too dark, with plugged shadows, while over-exposure (2c) is too light, with burnt-out highlights.

77

Rush Print Reports

Each laboratory has its own form of report sheet, but they all show exposure ratings of every scene printed, laboratory roll number and the original camera report. Subsequent work by the laboratory is facilitated if the original roll number is quoted whenever needed. Daily roll numbers are a convenient system for indexing laboratory material until it is finally assembled into an established cut reel under a title and part number.

Any physical defects such as rubs, scratches and dirt spots will also be reported; some of these may require further investigation to establish their exact location and cause. They may be noted (x), meaning 'to be checked' and further detailed information will follow. Wherever possible, the actual frame will be identified by its edge number.

Abbreviations

Position in the frame	:	TS	Track side (left hand side of screen)
		NTS	Non-track side (right hand side)
Film surface	:	Emul	Emulsion side of the film
		Cell	Celluloid (base) side of the film
Position in the take	:	HE	Head end, near the beginning
		TE	Tail end, near the end of the action
Character	:	−D	Minus Density, appears white
		+D	Plus Density, appears black
		Int	Intermittent, usually at frame period
		Irreg	Irregular, with no repeating period
		DA	Dirty Camera Aperture
Degree	:	VS	Very slight, hardly noticeable
		S or Sl	Slight, noticeable but not serious
		BN	Below normal, undesirable
		VBN	Very below normal, objectionable
		NG	No good, quite unacceptable

The report sheet may also note items in the action or composition which should be checked for acceptability by the editor. For example, camera focus pulling, microphones or their shadows appearing within the frame, and objects or movement being cut at the edge of the frame. Short period exposure variations ('flicker' or 'flutter'), irregularity of focus ('breathing') or unsteadiness of the image in the camera gate (horizontal 'weave' or vertical 'float') will also be reported, since these may indicate a fault in the camera mechanism.

Although the laboratory contact man may not have an opportunity to see every rush print, he will always be advised of the rush print viewer's comments and will check any doubtful items. He may add general overall comments (especially on exposure or photographic quality) to help the cameraman.

PRODUCER FOCAL PROD'NS **TITLE** "A NEW LOOK"
FOR THE ATTENTION OF. BERT COX **CAMERAMAN**
ROLL No 17604
NEGATIVE REPORT ON STUDIO RUSHES

EMUL AND EMUL No — VS Emul rub NTS HE Sq208 TK.2
E/C 5254
451-17

SIGNATURE Bey.B.

VIEWERS REPORT ON PRINT OF ABOVE NEGATIVE   DATE. 6 Nov 73
DAY, NIGHT, INTERIOR, EXTERIOR FIRELIGHT

SCENE	Take	Light	REMARKS	SCENE	Take	Light	REMARKS
207	2	26	FLICKER EFFECT				
208	2	26	"				
209	3	27					

Consignment No 12 — **RUSH PRINT VIEWING REPORT** — Prod. A NEW LOOK
Date of Photog. 5. xi.73 — Sold to FOCAL PROD:
FOR COLOUR/B&W — G.P.O. No 27512

Roll No	Camera Report or Your Order No	Scene & Take	Prints Required Col:	Rush Print B&W	Rush Print Timings	Final Rating	Comments
17604	3751	207-2	P		20.28.26	28	Yellow–Red for Firelight
		208-2	P		20.28.26	28	" "
		209	P		21.29.21		

Exposure O.K and Consistant. Emul rub does NOT show in Print. Dick Roe

---

LABORATORY REPORT   No 26207
PICTURE NEGATIVE

Viewed by B.C
PRODUCTION A. NEW LOOK — PRODUCER FOCAL PROD'S
CAMERAMAN BERT COX — STOCK E/2 451-17 — CAMERA Rpt No 3751 — DATE 5.xi.73

GENERAL COMM
Firelight F...
Throw...

SHIP TO: FOCA... HEN...

ROLL	SLATE	Take	Y	M	C	REMARKS	ROLL	SLATE	Take	Y	M	C	REMARKS
604	207	2	26	28	20	Firelight Flicker							
	208	2	26	28	20	"							
	209	3	27	29	21	"							
	210	1	27	29	21	"							

EXAMINED BY B.G.B.   DATE 6 Nov.73.

COMPANY FOCAL PROD'NS
PRODUCTION A NEW LOOK
CAMERAMAN B. COX — LAB. ROLL No 17604 — EMUL. No 451-17 — 5254 — DATE 6-11-73 — SHEET No 1
B&W/COLOUR

SCENE	TAKE	R	G	B	R	G	B	SCENE DETAILS	REMARKS
207	2	20	28	26				NT. Int. Firelite	Flicker Effect
208	2	20	28	26				"	"
209	3	21	29	27				"	"
210	1	21	29	27				"	"

NEGATIVE CONDITION REPORT
Slight rub non-touch side Sc. 208-2
does not print
Exposure O.K. D.B

SPECIAL DELIVERY INSTRUCTIONS

LABORATORY CONTACT FOR THE ABOVE WORK IS MR ROE

RUSH PRINT REPORTS   Detailed reports on all negative printed in each laboratory roll must be sent to the Cutting Room and the Cameraman. These will generally show the printer point values and/or exposure rating for each scene, together with comments on any defects reported.

Rush Print Delivery Reports

The laboratory reports on the production negative and the rush prints are normally delivered direct to the cutting room so that all the information is available at the time that rushes are screened. An additional copy is usually sent to the cameraman, together with any colour pilot or Cinex strips which are called for. The production office or production manager also needs details of the material processed, both negative developed and quantity printed, so that these can be checked against his copy of the original camera logs initiating the work. Subsequently, both these records will be compared with the invoices giving the processing charges made by the laboratory and sent to the accounting department.

In some cases, the report sheet for all purposes is provided by additional copies of the printing data sheet, but in others it is a separate rush print viewing record, of which additional carbon copies carry the further information of the lengths of film processed in the separate categories for accounting purposes. All reports and delivery sheets will, of course, normally carry a serial number allocated by the laboratory for subsequent cross-reference and follow-up as required.

Negative defects

One of the subjects which may require a follow-up report is that of defects on the original negative. When a serious fault is noted in the course of viewing the rush print it is always necessary to investigate its source and to determine whether it can be cured or alleviated, and this check may not have been completed by the time the rush prints and their report are despatched to the studio. If the source of the defect is a purely temporary one, the cutting room will be advised to ignore the fault on the rush print or a reprint will be supplied. However, if the negative defect is likely to be permanent and objectionable, the editor must be advised of its exact location in the scene and take so that he may design his cutting to avoid that section or make use of an alternative take. A supplementary defect report giving these details will therefore be sent to the cutting room as soon as the examination of the negative has been completed, although this procedure is only necessary for major defects whose appearance on the screen is obvious.

RUSH PRINT DELIVERY REPORT FOR COLOUR/B & W

Consignment No. 12
Date of Photography 5.xi.73
Date Prints Shipped 6.xi.73

Prod. 'A NEW LOOK'
Sold to FOCAL PROD'NS
G.P.O. Nº 27513

ROLL Nº	CAMERA REPORT OR YOUR ORDER Nº	SCENE & TAKE	PRINTS REQUIRED		B&W PRINT FOOTAGE FROM			COLOUR PRINT FOOTAGE			NEGATIVE DEVELOPED FOOTAGE
			COL	B&W	E'COLOR NEGATIVE	OTHER NEGATIVE	TRACK NEGATIVE	UNCORRECTED E'COLOR	CORRECTED R'COLOR		
17604	3751	207-2	P						35		310
		208-2	P						20		
		209-3	P						35		
		210-1	P						2 ь		
17605	3751	207-3	P	30							
		211-3	P	30							
	TOTAL FOOTAGE			60					160		310
	PRICE										
	VALUE										
	CODE										

SHIP TO FOCAL CUTTING ROOMS, HENSHAW STUDIOS

BY: VAN
VIA: ELSTREE

RECEIVED THE ABOVE
W. Rimmu
Signature
12740

1

**ADDITIONAL REPORT ON NEGATIVE DEFECTS
SEE ALSO OUR VIEWING REPORTS Nos 25713**

To The Editor, FOCAL CUTTING ROOMS   Date 16.OCT.1973

Copies Production Manager   Subject A NEW LOOK
FOCAL PROD'NS.
(Stock Manufacturers)   Photographed 15.OCT.1973

          Company FOCAL PRODUCTIONS LTD.

Roll No.	Scene	Take	Nature and Position of Defect (Edge Nºs)	REMARKS
16213	185	1	Severe pre-developed emulsion scratches on track side over least 10 feet of Slate 185-1 and throughout Take 2. Also severe pre-developed crease across two frames at edge Nº E9X 249214²⁺³ SUSPECTED MANUFACTURING ORIGIN	This section considered NG for production use.
	185	2		
			Section affected E9X 249138 to 155 Emulsion 5254-451-15 Strip Nº16 Perforator Nº56	

2

RUSH PRINT DELIVERY REPORTS   A separate Delivery Report (1) covering a number of rush print rolls is sometimes sent to Cutting Room and Production Manager. Follow-up reports on negative defects requiring detailed investigation may also be supplied (2).

Negative Movement Records & Reprints

A detailed record of the identification and movement of each scene of negative is of great importance for later stages of laboratory work. It ensures that all the material required for the final cutting of the production can be brought together rapidly and efficiently. In some organisations this is simply done by a scene list, giving the laboratory rush print roll number for every scene and take in numerical order, although if this is to include an edge number identification a considerable amount of transcription of records is involved. An alternative system, much used for 16mm material, is merely to list the first and last edge numbers of all originals received in numerical order with the laboratory roll numbers to correspond. 16mm original rolls are usually not broken down into individual scenes and takes for storage, but are retained in their assembled rolls to minimise handling and possible damage.

Reprints

Other laboratories use a carbon copy of the information recorded at the initial break-down of the original camera roll into its scenes for printing. As described earlier, the breakdown operator notes the starting and ending edge numbers for each printed take when preparing the rush print roll, so a copy of this provides the basic record for all subsequent use of each section of negative. These further stages may include the break-down of the rush print roll into its individual scenes for storage, any reprints which may be required by the editor to replace material damaged or extensively re-cut in editing, scenes duplicated in optical effect rolls, and the final disposition of the scene, part of which may appear in the finally edited cutting copy, the remainder (the 'trims') being stored for eventual return to the production company. All these succeeding operations must be recorded as part of the history of the negative movement. In general, the original roll of negative made up for rush printing is held in its complete form for a few days after the initial prints have been delivered, in case any immediate reprints are required by the production company, either by the editor for cutting room purposes or by the cameraman for revised grading. After this period, reprints for any purpose ordered later may require the retrieval of the required section of negative from break-down storage as an individual scene and make-up afresh. Similarly, a request for a previously unprinted scene ('second negative') will require its make-up under a new roll number.

Reprint scenes are not usually called for by the cutting rooms on any standard form but merely as a numbered order giving details of the requirement. From their records of negative movement to date, the laboratory will identify the location of the material called for so that it can be withdrawn from storage and made-up into a new roll for printing.

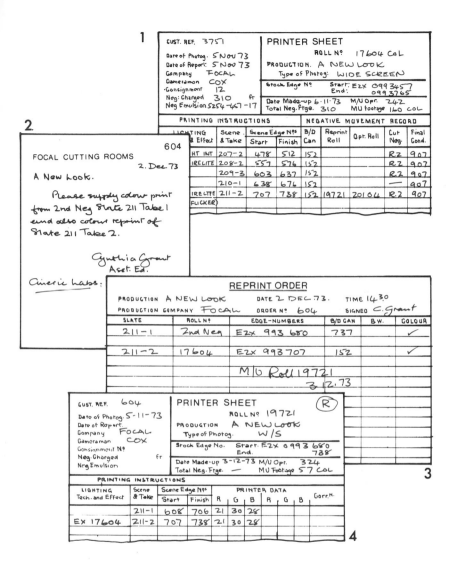

NEGATIVE MOVEMENT RECORDS A further copy of the initial break-down record can be used to note subsequent movements of each individual scene and take (1). A reprint order from the Cutting Room (2) requires the laboratory to locate the scenes required (3) and make them up in a new roll for printing (4).

Negative Storage Records

After rush printing the rolls of 35mm negative are generally broken down into their individual scenes and takes for convenient storage and easy selection when required. These comparatively short lengths should always be wound on 2 inch diameter cores with a few feet of waste film on the inside and outside for protection. For ready reference, a breakdown tab is made out for each take giving its identification and storage location, and folded round the outer strip of the protective spacing. This both labels each small roll for recognition, and secures it against unwinding in the storage can. When selected scenes and takes are picked for final negative cutting, these tabs allow the rolls to be set out in continuity order and the details of their final usage by part number and cut numbers can be entered to assist the work of the cutter.

Broken-down takes are generally stored flat in rectangular cans, each can being numbered and given a record sheet with details of its contents and their subsequent use prior to final assembly. Similarly, second negative not specified for printing on the original camera log is stored in another series of cans with their own identification and records. To save storage space, the second negative scenes from several days work may be wound on one core and stored in a large circular can. This assembly without splicing is termed 'condensing' and normally precedes the return of the unwanted takes to the production company.

Storage by customers

In many laboratories storage space is so limited that all original material, both printed takes and second negative, must be returned to the customer for storage until further work is required. It is very common to return 16mm film, where further stages of preparatory work (up to final cutting) are often carried out by independent specialist houses. The laboratories initial roll identification should be preserved wherever possible or cross-references provided so that the rush printing data can be identified.

Original material returned to the laboratory for further work should be carefully packed in a can and identified on the label; if the can is taped it should always be only across the top and bottom, never around the edge, to distinguish it from exposed film sent in for processing.

Processed film should be stored just as carefully as raw stock: high temperatures and high humidity must be avoided, even for comparatively short storage periods. The preferred conditions are approximately 70°F (22°C) at 50 per cent relative humidity or less. If processed rolls of film have been stored at very low temperatures or refrigerated for any lengthy period they should be brought up to normal room temperature quite slowly, over a period of several hours, to prevent moisture condensation on their surfaces.

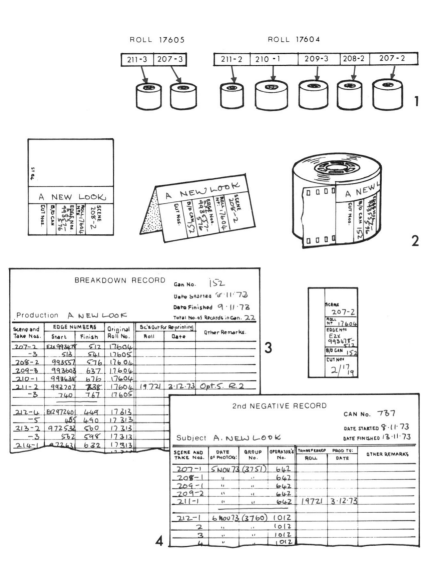

ROLL 17605   ROLL 17604

| 211-3 | 207-3 | | 211-2 | 210-1 | 209-3 | 208-2 | 207-2 |

1

2

BREAKDOWN RECORD Can No. 152

Date Started 8·11·73
Date Finished 9·11·73

Production A NEW LOOK

Total No. of Records in Can. 22

Scene and Take Nos.	EDGE NUMBERS Start	Finish	Original Roll No.	Sc's Out for Re-printing Roll	Date	Other Remarks.
207-2	E2x 99347	512	17604			
-3	513	541	17605			
208-2	993557	576	17604			
209-3	993603	637	17604			
210-1	993638	676	17604			
211-2	993707	738	17604	19721	2·12·73	Opt.5. R.2
-3	740	767	17605			
212-4	B297240	449	17313			
-5	455	490	17313			
213-2	972532	560	17313			
-3	562	598	17313			
214-1	B7263	632	17313			

3

SCENE 207-2
ROLL Nº 17604
EDGE Nos E2x 993475-512
B/D CAN 152
CUT Nos
2/17 19

2nd NEGATIVE RECORD CAN No. 737

DATE STARTED 8·11·73
DATE FINISHED 13·11·73

Subject A. NEW LOOK

SCENE AND TAKE Nos.	DATE of PHOTOG:	GROUP No.	OPERATOR'S No.	TRANSFERRED Roll	PROD TO: Date	OTHER REMARKS
207-1	5 NOV 73	(3751)	642			
208-1	"	"	642			
209-1	"	"	642			
209-2	"	"	642			
211-1	"	"	642	19721	3·12·73	
212-1	6 NOV 73	(3760)	1012			
2	"	"	1012			
3	"	"	1012			
4	"	"	1012			

4

NEGATIVE STORAGE RECORDS   After printing the netative rolls are broken down into individual scenes, wound on cores (1) and given identification tabs (2). The Break-down Record Sheet (3) lists the contents of each storage can. Unprinted Second Negative is recorded separately (4).

85

Simplified Record Systems

The procedures outlined in the previous pages represent practices established to provide a full service to feature film studios wishing to rely on the laboratory for all film handling and records. Many details can be eliminated and the whole system stream-lined where the production organisation is prepared to take over everything except the actual processing and printing. The original camera logs themselves can also be simplified where operations are well standardised in a regular routine, as should normally occur for the production of TV series, for example, when only one-light colour rushes are to be made in all cases.

Laboratory records can be simplified if the printed takes from several negative rolls are made up for printing together, the break-down operator allocating one processing daily roll number to contain as many scenes as convenient. Negative edge numbers from the beginning of each printed take are recorded as the scenes are made up, and a copy of the make-up record sheet becomes the instruction sheet for the printer.

The approved one-light printing values for the subject are then added to the record and the whole roll printed at this level. A further copy of the record sheet then becomes available for the rush print viewer's use. After viewing, the print is delivered to the production company's cutting room with a copy of the same record sheet for use by the editor. No other viewing reports are provided unless there are specific negative defects to be investigated. The cameraman is left to make his own assessment of exposure from the appearance of the one-light rush print.

Returning film to the production company

Unprinted takes from the developed negative rolls are returned to the studio immediately, usually with the rush prints of the selected takes, with no further break-down or records. Printed takes are held until the rush prints have been delivered and viewed by the production company in case reprints are required by the editor, but then the made-up negative rolls are sent back to the studio identified only with their laboratory roll number, for which the record sheets have already been supplied. If reprints are required at a later date the appropriate negative is sent to the laboratory with the reprint order.

This whole procedure transfers the responsibility for all negative identification and storage from the laboratory to the production company and is normally followed by the handling of all subsequent operations, the preparation of opticals and special effects and the selection and final cutting of the negative also being undertaken by the producer's organisation.

FOCAL T.V.   3751

PRODUCTION 'A NEW LOOK'
CAMERAMAN B. COX   DIRECTOR A. BOX
ROLL No (17604)   PRINT CIRCLED TAKES ONLY

SCENE	TAKE	FOOTAGE Camera total	FOOTAGE Taken each	REMARKS
207	1	20	20	NITE INT
	(2)	55	55	
	(3)	85	30	
208	1	100	15	
	(2)	120	20	
209	1	130	10	
	2	145	15	
	(3)	180	35	
210	(1)	220	40	
211	1	250	30	
	(2)	280	30	
	(3)	310	30	

	FOOTAGE	
GOOD	220	CAMERA No A.317
N.G	90	MAG No 414
WASTE	90	RECORD No
TOTAL	400	EMUL No 451-17

FOCAL T.V.   3752

PRODUCTION 'A NEW LOOK'
CAMERAMAN B. COX   DIRECTOR A. BOX
ROLL No (17604)   PRINT CIRCLED TAKES ONLY

SCENE	TAKE	FOOTAGE Camera total	FOOTAGE Taken each	REMARKS
212	1	20	20	NITE INT
	2	48	28	
	3	88	40	
	(4)	136	48	
213	(5)	176	40	
213	1	196	20	
	(2)	224	28	
	(3)	260	36	
214	(1)	292	32	
215	1	326	34	
	(2)	375	49	

	FOOTAGE	
GOOD	233	CAMERA No A.317
N.G	142	MAG No 456
WASTE	25	RECORD No
TOTAL	400	EMUL No 451-17

DATE 5.NOV	ROLL No 17604	COMPANY FOCAL	PRODUCTION NEW LOOK	REQ No 3751/2

Y	C	M		SCENE	FTG.	D	N	KEY NUMBER
26	20	28	1	207-2	35		✓	993478
			2	-3	30		✓	513
			3	208-2	20		✓	557
			4	209-3	35		✓	603
			5	210-1	40		✓	638
			6	211-2	30		✓	707
			7	-3	30		✓	740
			8	212-4	48		✓	972 401
			9	-5	40		✓	450
			10	213-2	28		✓	532
			11	-3	36		✓	562
			12	214-1	32		✓	599
			13	215-2	49		✓	664
			14					

ONE-LITE

1-LITE TIMED COLOR PRINT   453'   INTERPOS. REGISTERED
COLOR CORR. PRINT   NEG. FTG.

2398

SIMPLIFIED RECORDS   In a simplified system the chosen takes from two or more camera reports (1) and (2), are made up in one roll for printing. Multiple copies of a single record sheet (3) serve as printing instructions, viewing report, delivery note and editor's record.

Opticals: Transition Effects

As the work of editing proceeds, it will often be found that visual effects are required which could not be undertaken by direct photography at the time of shooting. The most frequently needed of these are transitional effects used to link the action of different sequences: Fades, Dissolves or Mixes, and Wipes. These provide a form of visual punctuation in the telling of the story.

Fades
The normal scene gradually darkens to a uniform black (Fade-Out) or a uniform black changes to a normal scene (Fade-in). Traditionally, a fade-in was the accepted manner of opening a motion picture presentation, while a fade-out followed by a fade-in represented the most marked division between two sequences of the action.

Dissolves
The first scene ('out-going') mixes imperceptibly to the second scene ('in-coming') over a length of time during which the whole of both scenes are visible to some extent. Dissolves thus provides a much closer link between the content of two sequences than is afforded by fade-in/fade-out, while still indicating a transition of action.

Wipes
Both scenes are seen together for a short period, but in this case a boundary moves across the frame revealing the new incoming scene behind it and 'wiping off' the first outgoing scene by its passage. The moving boundary between the two scenes can be a sharply-defined line ('Hard-edge wipe') or diffuse so that the two are partially superimposed at the edge ('soft-edge wipe'). Wipes are made in a great variety of forms, with the edge moving horizontally, vertically or diagonally across the frame or in complex patterns; those with a circular outline are known as 'iris wipes'. Two or more moving edges may be used, for example a pair of vertical lines opening from the centre of the screen ('barn-door wipe') or rotating from a point on the edge ('fan wipe'), and reference must be made to the 'pattern chart' issued by many laboratories and effects specialists for the whole range of varieties available. Wipe effects are now rare in feature films, but are widely used in publicity films and advertising shorts.

The preparation of any of these effects usually involves the preparation of a duplicate negative and at one time all work of this type was done on an optical step printer. Although this is no longer always the case, the term 'optical' has been retained as a general term for laboratory effects. The correct specification of such effects is an important part of cutting room work in its laboratory relations.

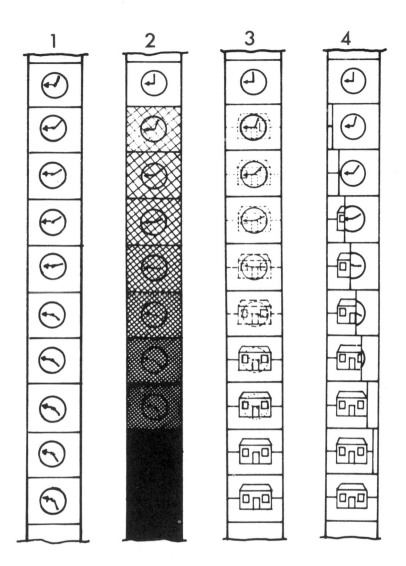

OPTICALS : TRANSITION EFFECTS (1) The original scene as photographed.
(2) Fade-out to black screen ; the opposite effect, from black screen to normal
picture is a Fade-in. (3) Dissolve or Mix, the image of the first scene becoming
fainter as it is replaced by that of the second becoming clearer. (4) Wipe : the
first scene is gradually replaced by the second at a boundary edge moving across
the frame.

89

Opticals: Other Special Effects

In addition to transitions, other special effects may be required for dramatic or continuity purposes.

Changes of action are usually described as follows:—

Stop Frame: (Freeze Frame, Hold Frame): a single picture image of the negative is repeated for a number of frames so that the action appears stationary when the print is projected. Alternating between two or three adjacent frames (provided that there is no perceptible movement between them) may provide a smoother result with less objectionable grain. For three frames the repeated sequence 1.2.3.2.1.2.3.2.1, etc. is preferred.

Skip Frame: to speed up the rate of the original action by printing only every other frame (2 : 1 skip) or every third (3 : 1 skip), so that it appears at double or treble normal speed when projected.

Stretch Frame: here the action is slowed down by repeating each individual frame twice or even three times. A special variation is used when old silent films photographed at 16 pictures per second are duplicated for projection at sound speed, 24 p.p.s. Only the odd frames are duplicated, so that the original series 1,2,3,4 is printed as 1,1,2,3,3,4. This may give rise to a somewhat jerky appearance and a better way is to make the additional frames by a combination exposure of two originals, as 1, 1+2, 2,3,3+4,4.

Reverse Action: the original action can be shown backwards if the sequence of frames is reversed, so that the last image appears first. Merely running the film tail first will, of course, make the picture appear upside down as well.

Image size and position changes that may be required are:—

Blow-up: the enlargement of a part of the image to fill the whole frame, either to give a more close-up shot or to eliminate an unwanted object, such as a microphone, from the very edge of the picture. It is important to specify the exact area of the frame to be enlarged very clearly. Magnifications of two times or more may show rather noticeable grain.

Zoom: the enlargement factor is gradually increased frame by frame to give the effect of a zoom-lens shot.

Flop-over: the direction of the action is reversed from left right, as though seen in a mirror (NOT to be confused with Reverse Action in time).

Diffusion, Out-of-Focus, Star and Ripple Effects: Image changes similar to those obtained in the camera can be introduced by the laboratory and if necessary combined with other transitions.

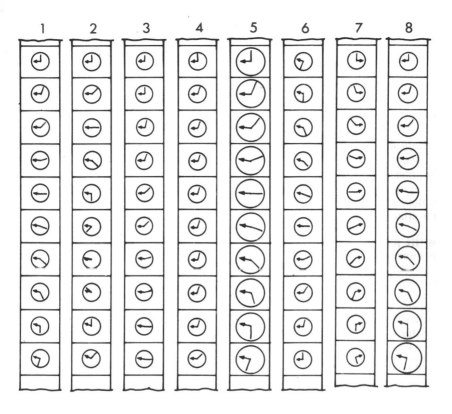

OPTICAL EFFECTS   (1) The original scene as photographed. (2) Skip Frame, printing every other frame. (3) Stretch Frame, each frame printed twice. (4) Stop Frame, the same frame repeated as long as required. (5) Blow-up, part of the image enlarged to fill the frame. (6) Reverse Action, the sequence of frames reversed, so that the action goes backwards. (7) Flop-over, the action reversed from right to left. (8) Zoom, the image grows larger frame by frame.

Opticals: Image Combination

Many laboratory optical effects involve the combination of two or more images. The simplest of these is straight-forward *superimposition* by double-printing, so that both images are visible. The relative importance of the two images is usually specified as a percentage, 50-50 representing them equally balanced but the character of the subjects is very important and a light scene will tend to dominate over a uniformly dark one. Titles superimposed on an action background, whether as white letters or in colour, are widely used.

Many combined image effects involve the use of Mattes, which are film images with opaque areas of heavy density used to prevent printing in selected areas of the frame; their positions may be fixed or moving to follow some part of the action ('travelling mattes') and their edges may be sharp ('hard') or diffused ('soft edge matte').

Split screen shots

A simple example of the fixed matte is a split-screen shot, portions of two scenes being combined by the use of a pair of complementary mattes, one reserving an unexposed area when printing the first scene, while the other protects those printed areas when the second scene is exposed. Split screen shots of two dissimilar scenes with a visible soft-edge boundary may be used in editing for simultaneous action, or the edge may be invisible, as in trick shots showing the same actor playing two roles. Photographed paintings or models can also be combined with studio action by the use of mattes to avoid the cost of building very large sets.

Adding background to studio shots

The most important application of moving mattes is in shots where an actor photographed in the studio is to be shown against a live background photographed on location at another time. For this work a pair of complementary mattes representing the foreground action in silhouette must be obtained, one with the action opaque on a clear background and the other showing the action as a clear area on an opaque background. The systems of photography used as a starting point for this Travelling Matte work, mostly involve coloured or specially illuminated uniform backgrounds behind the foreground actors. But details of these and the preparation of combination images are really the province of the specialist trick effects organisation and fall outside the normal range of laboratory processing.

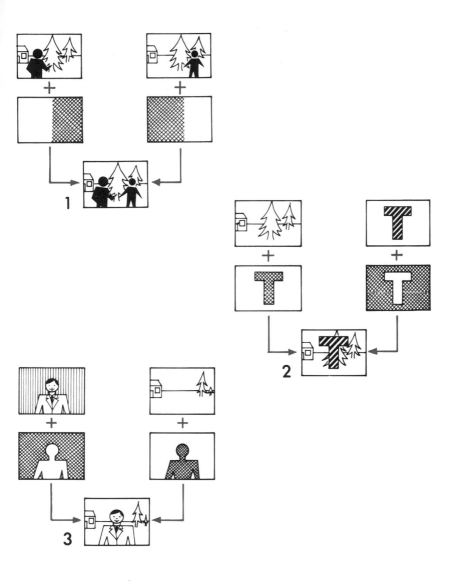

IMAGE COMBINATION   A number of optical special effects involve the use of pairs of complementary mattes to reserve areas of the frame during printing from the two scenes. (1) Split-screen Effect; (2) Coloured Letter Title superimposed on a real scene background; (3) Travelling Matte: a moving subject can be superimposed on a background scene by using mattes whose outlines follow the foreground action.

Markings for Optical Effects

It is essential that clear instructions are provided, preferably both on the cutting copy and as written specifications. It is recommended that work print markings should be made in yellow grease pencil only, to differentiate them from other signs and cues that the editor may use in mixing and dubbing which should be in red or black.

Fades
Fades should be indicated by two converging lines, the point of the 'V' being at the frame where the fade is to be totally black ('start fade in' or 'fade full out'). Where a fade-out is to be followed immediately by a fade-in, the points of the two 'V's' will normally be at the splice between the two scenes where the picture is completely dark. The open end of the 'V' must indicate the point at which the picture is a normal image ('start fade out' or 'fade full in'). Automatic equipment is usually available on laboratory machines to print fades of standard lengths of 1, $1\frac{1}{2}$, 2, 3, and 4 feet (16, 24, 32, 48, 64 frames), but this should be checked with the laboratory concerned before ordering.

Dissolves
Dissolves are marked either by a pair of superimposed fade V's or by a single line from one side of the film to the other and back again. In both cases the start and finish of the marks should indicate the beginning and end of the mix and the splice between the two scenes in the cutting copy should be at the centre of the effect. As with fades, dissolves are usually made of standard lengths and should be specified accordingly.

Wipes
Specifications are so varied that written instructions should always be given; when marked on the work print, a single diagonal line showing its length with a reference to the laboratory wipe pattern number is sometimes used.

Hold and freeze frames
A hold frame or freeze frame will usually be indicated by a cross on the frame to be repeated, followed by an arrow through a number of frames of black spacing to indicate the length over which it is to be held.

Other effects
Simple superimposition titles and double-exposure effects can be indicated by cutting in a few frames of the superimposed scene into the background scene at the points where the effect is to begin and end, their overall length being marked by a wavy line. It is essential that at least one of these cut-in sections is long enough to include a stock edge-number on the print to permit negative matching.

94

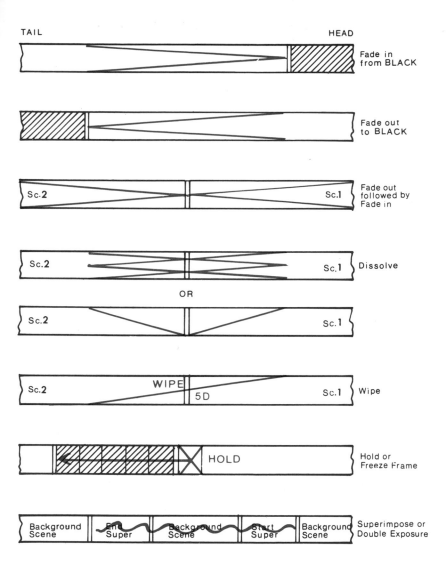

TAIL   HEAD

Fade in from BLACK

Fade out to BLACK

Sc.2   Sc.1   Fade out followed by Fade in

Sc.2   Sc.1   Dissolve

OR

Sc.2   Sc.1

WIPE
5D   Sc.2   Sc.1   Wipe

HOLD   Hold or Freeze Frame

Background Scene   End Super   Background Scene   Start Super   Background Scene   Superimpose or Double Exposure

MARKINGS FOR OPTICAL EFFECTS   The required length and position of optical effects such as fades, dissolves, wipes, etc, should be clearly marked on the work print in the manner shown, preferably using a yellow grease-pencil.

Specifications for Optical Work

The specification for optical work should be formal instruction to the laboratory, confirming and amplifying any cutting copy markings. The specification and work print must be in exact agreement.

The specification must show the scene and take number, the location by edge numbers within the scene, the effect required and its length.

The following abbreviations are generally adopted:—

At the beginning, SFO   Start Fade Out SFI Start Fade In
SDO   Start Dissolve Out SDI Start Dissolve In
At the end,   FFO   Fade Full Out FFI Fade Full In
DFO   Dissolve Full Out DFI Dissolve Full In.

It is also helpful to have the editor's reference number for the optical and the cut reel for which it is intended, if known. Present practice (to save expense) is to make duplicate negatives only slightly longer than the actual effect required, and to cut them into the original negative of the rest of the scene. However, if the length of the scene as cut is less than 3 feet beyond the start or finish of the optical, it is usual to extend the dupe to cover this length. In such cases, the beginning or end of the cut scene should be specified, allowing additional frames for subsequent handling.

Examples

In the first example, scene 211 Take 2 is used with a fade-out 2 feet long ending 12 frames after the edge number marked frame E2X 993732. Strictly this is all that is required but the start of the cut is given as 728.

The second example is for a 2 foot fade-in on scene 242–5, starting with a completely black frame 12 frames before edge number E1X 246791 and becoming normal at 3 frames after 792. As noted earlier the first frame of this may be marked either as 12 frames before 791 or as 4 frames after 790, but as edge number 790 itself does not appear in the cutting copy, the reference 12 frames before 791 is better. The third example requests a 3 foot mix from scene 244–2 to scene 255–4, with its centre on the splice between E1X 246844 plus 2 frames for the first (put-going) scene and 4 frames before E1X 348902 for the second (in-coming) scene. The frames corresponding to the start of the dissolve out (S.D.O.) of the first scene and the end of the dissolve (D.F.I.) of the second are in the cutting copy, but the end of the out-going dissolve (D.F.O.) and the start of the incoming (S.D.I.) are not. Their specification must therefore be derived by counting forward from the splice on the first scene and backward from the splice on the second. Where a long dissolve is specified near the beginning or end of the action of a take it is advisable to check these "hidden' frames, since it may be found on cutting that there is insufficient negative to cover the dissolve.

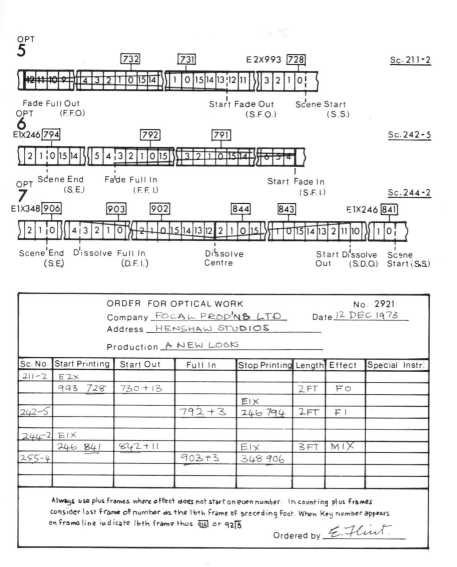

OPT **5**

732   731   E 2X993 728   Sc. 211-2

| 12 | 11 | 10 | 9 | | 4 | 3 | 2 | 1 | 0 | 15 | 14 | | 1 | 0 | 15 | 14 | 13 | 12 | 11 | | 3 | 2 | 1 | 0 |

Fade Full Out   Start Fade Out   Scene Start
(F.F.O.)   (S.F.O.)   (S.S.)

OPT **6**

E1X246 794   792   791   Sc. 242-5

| 2 | 1 | 0 | 15 | 14 | | 5 | 4 | 3 | 2 | 1 | 0 | 15 | | 3 | 2 | 1 | 0 | 15 | 14 | | 6 | 5 | 4 |

Scene End   Fade Full In   Start Fade In
(S.E.)   (F.F.I.)   (S.F.I.)

OPT **7**

E1X348 906   903   902   844   843   E1X246 841   Sc. 244-2

| 2 | 1 | 0 | | 4 | 3 | 2 | 1 | 0 | | 2 | 1 | 0 | 15 | 14 | 13 | 12 | 2 | 1 | 0 | 15 | | 1 | 0 | 15 | 14 | 13 | 2 | 11 | 10 | | 1 | 0 |

Scene End   Dissolve Full In   Dissolve   Start Dissolve   Scene
(S.E.)   (D.F.I.)   Centre   Out   (S.D.O.)   Start (S.S.)

ORDER FOR OPTICAL WORK   No. 2921

Company _FOCAL PROD'NS LTD_   Date _12 DEC 1973_

Address _HENSHAW STUDIOS_

Production _A NEW LOOK_

Sc. No.	Start Printing	Start Out	Full In	Stop Printing	Length	Effect	Special Instr.
211-2	E2X						
	993 728	730 + 13			2 FT	FO	
				E1X			
242-5			792 + 3	246 794	2 FT	F I	
244-2	E1X						
	246 841	842 + 11		E1X	3 FT	MIX	
255-4			903 + 3	348 906			

Always use plus frames where effect does not start on even number. In counting plus frames consider last frame of number as the 16th frame of preceding foot. When Key number appears on frame line indicate 16th frame thus 92̄5̄ or 92|5̄

Ordered by _E. Flint._

SPECIFICATIONS FOR OPTICAL WORK   (1) The cutting copy markings and edge number identifications for three optical effects: Opt.5 Fade-out, Opt.6 Fade-in, Opt.7 Dissolve. (2) The laboratory order for optical work covering these three effects.

Optical Specification Sheets (1)

Different laboratories make use of differing forms on which to specify optical work and the following pages show completed examples of these. Each has been made out to cover the same three opticals outlined on the preceding page and it may be of interest to compare the representation of the cutting copy with various specification sheets, each of which presents the same instructions in slightly different form. In all cases the sheet covers three opticals, numbers 5, 6, and 7, for the finally cut negative of Reel 2.

First example
Both the beginning and the end frames of the fade-out and fade-in are given as well as the length of the fade effect required and for the dissolve both the 'hidden' SDI and DFO frames are given as well as those which appear in the cutting copy for SDO and DFI. All frames are given in the form $\underline{730} + 13$ rather than 3 frames before $\underline{731}$, written $\underline{731}$–4, because of the ambiguity of the minus sign, –. Scene starts and ends are given to the nearest full edge number, indicating that the final cutting point is not yet decided.

Second example
Only the frames at the spliced end of the fade-out (FFO) or fade-in (SFI) are given together with the length of the effect. For the dissolve only the extreme 'cutting copy' frames SDO and DFI are given and the 'hidden' frames must be checked by the laboratory on making up the material. This type of sheet also contains some information on grading and the original daily rush print roll from which the negative is to be derived, which will of course be entered from the laboratories' records.

OPTICAL DEPARTMENT

Prod A NEW LOOK   Reel No 2   Date 12 Dec 73

OPT. No.	SCENE + TAKE	EFFECT	SCENE START/END	EFFECT START/END	
5	211-2	2'-F.O.	SS. E2x 993 [728]	S.F.O. [730]+13	
				F.F.O. [732]+12	
6	242-5	2' F.I.		S.F.I [790]+4	
				F.F.I. [792]+3	
			S.E. E1x 246 [794]		
7	244-2	3' MIX	S.S. E1x 246 [841]	S.D.O. [842]+11	
				[845]+10	
	255-4	To		[900]+4	
				[903]+3	
			S.E E1x 348 [906]		

OPTICAL SPECIFICATION

SUBJECT A. NEW LOOK   DATE 12 xii 73   ORDER No. 2921

PRODUCER FOCAL PROD'NS   EDITOR E. FLINT

ROLL No.	OPT No.	FOR REEL	SCENE AND TAKE	SCENE START OR START FADE IN	LEN. OF FADE	START DISSOLVE OUT	LENGTH OF DISSOLVE	END DISSOLVE IN	SCENE END OR FADE FULL OUT	LEN. OF FADE	TIME OF DAY REQD.	ORIGINAL ROLL	TYPE OF NEG.	LENG. OF SCENE	FILM LOCATION
20104	5	2	211-2	SS E2x 993 [728]					FFO [732]+12	2'	INT Nite	17604	E/c	31'	B/D 152
	6	2	242-5	SFI E2x 246 [790] +4	2'				SE E1x 246 [794]		INT DAY	18355	E/c	25'	B/D 176
	7	2	244-2	SS E1x 246 [841]		SDO [842]+11	3'				INT DAY	18355	E/c	20'	B/D 176
			MIX TO 255-4					DFI [903]+3	SE E1x 348 [906]		EXT DAY	18371	E/c	32'	193

SPECIAL INSTRUCTIONS

OPTICAL SPECIFICATION SHEETS (1)   The three opticals described on the previous page may be specified in various forms for different laboratories. The second example above includes information for the location of the negative required from Storage.

Optical Specification Sheets (2)

The same three opticals are specified on the other types of form shown here; these can be filled in directly from the marked cutting copy since the only frames to be identified are those which are actually visible in the work print. It will be noted that in one case the frame identification is spelt out in full ' . . . FRAMES BEFORE (or AFTER) KEY NO. . . .,' so that the number read on the print can always be quoted. In the second case the same information is to be shown as 'Key No.........................+.................. Frames' or 'Key No.......................–...........Frames.' In both forms all effects are specified by the frames adjacent to the work print splices: the End of a Fade-out, the Start of a Fade-in and the centre of a Dissolve or wipe.

Additional reminders
There is a reminder of the necessity of indicating the portion of the edge number opposite the frame taken as zero by boxing, as shown and on one of the forms an indication of the preferred practice for that laboratory of duping the whole length of the scene if it is less than 10 feet before or after the optical effect itself.

FROM   FOCAL PRODNS   Nº 0651

TO.
       CINERIC LABORATORIES

       OPTICAL EFFECTS DEPARTMENT

Production A. NEW LOOK   Reel Nº 2   Date 12 DEC. 73.

IMPORTANT: Zero Frame must be indicated by boxing in the following way :- 14 Y G41 511 or 14 Y 841 511 or 14 Y G41 511.

We advise that if length of scene before or after optical is less than appox.10 ft., then the whole scene should be marked for duping.	SPECIAL INSTRUCTIONS
SCENE AND TAKE Nº 211-2 START DUPE AT KEY NºE2x 993 720	
END 2 FT. FADEOUT AT 12 FRAMES AFTER KEY Nº 995 732	opt.
START FT. FADE IN AT FRAMES BEFORE KEY Nº	5
CENTRE OF FT MIX/WIPE { FRAMES AFTER KEY Nº and FRAMES BEFORE KEY Nº	
SCENE AND TAKE Nº END DUPE AT KEY Nº	
SCENE AND TAKE Nº 242-5 START DUPE AT KEY Nº	
END FT FADE OUT AT FRAMES AFTER KEY Nº	opt
START 2 FT FADE IN AT 12 FRAMES BEFORE KEY NºEIX 246 791	6
CENTRE OF FT MIX/WIPE { FRAMES AFTER KEY Nº and FRAMES BEFORE KEY Nº	
SCENE AND TAKE Nº END DUPE AT KEY Nº 246 796	

Second form (overlapping):

A	SPECIAL INSTRUCTIONS	
Scene and Take Nº 211-2 (5)	Opticals 5, 6, 7,	Nº EIX 246 841
Start Dupe at Key Nº E2X 993 728	Complete Reel 2	Nº
End Fr Fade out at Key Nº E2X 993 732 +12 Frames	E7	Nº
Start Fr Fade In at Key Nº — Frames		Nº 246 844 opt
Centre of Fr Dissolve/Wipe at { Key Nº + Frames / Key Nº — Frames		Nº EIX 348 902 7
Incoming Scene and Take Nº		Nº EIX 348 904
End Dupe at Key Nº		Nº

B		
Scene and Take Nº 242-5 (6)		Nº
Start Dupe at Key Nº		Nº
End Fr Fade out at Key Nº + Frames		Nº
Start 2 Ft Fade In at Key Nº EIX 246 791 —12 Frames		Nº
Centre of Fr Dissolve/Wipe at { Key Nº + Frames / Key Nº — Frames		Nº
Incoming Scene and Take Nº		Nº
End Dupe at Key Nº EIX 246 794		

C	
Scene and Take Nº 244-2 (7)	
Start Dupe at Key Nº EIX 246 841	
End Fr Fade Out at Key Nº + Frames	
Start Fr Fade In at Key Nº — Frames	
Centre of 3 Ft Dissolve/Wipe at { Key NºEIX 246 844 + 2 Frames / Key Nº EIX 348 902 — 4 Frames	
Incoming Scene and Take Nº 255-4	
End Dupe at Key Nº EIX 348 906	

Signed. Eric Flint

OPTICAL SPECIFICATION SHEETS (2)   Further examples of the specification
sheets from different laboratories completed for the same three optical effects
previously described.

Optical Specification Sheets (3)

Yet another variety of optical specification sheet is shown here, again completed for the three effects. As in the immediately preceding examples only the frames adjacent to the cutting copy splices need to be identified and the edge number zero frames to be quoted as those visible on the work print, in the form '.................Clear Frames After Key No. ....' for an outgoing scene or '.................Clear Frames Before Key No. ....' for an incoming one.

Although all these optical specifications appear very different at first sight, the principal information called for is the same in every case and no cutting room assistant should find any difficulty in completing any type once the basic principles have been understood.

A & B Printing

Optical effects of all types for 35mm photography are generally produced in the laboratory by the preparation of a duplicate negative which is eventually assembled with the original scenes at the final negative cutting stage. However, fades, dissolves and superimposed white titles can be produced by double-printing from the original in the final positive and this procedure, known as A & B Printing, is much used for 16mm productions, especially those photographed as reversal originals. The requirements for cutting to allow this system of printing are dealt with later and the next step to be considered will be the preparation of duplicate negatives for optical effects.

From _FOCAL PRODNS_   № 5404

To: _CINERIC LABS_

OPTICAL EFFECTS DEPT.

Prod A NEW LOOK   Reel No. 2   Date 2/12/73

Scene and Take No. 211-2 _____ CUT 12 _____ Clear Frames	**SPECIAL INSTRUCTIONS** *(if any)*
After Key No. E2X 993 [732]	

From {
_____ft. DISSOLVE*   2 ft. FADE OUT*
_____ft. WIPE No.*_____   _____ft. FADE IN*

Start Dupe
E2X 993728
(5)

To {
Scene and Take No._____ CUT_____ Clear Frames
Before Key No. _____

Scene and Take No._____ CUT_____ Clear Frames
After Key No._____

From {
_____ft. DISSOLVE*   _____ft. FADE OUT*
_____ft. WIPE No.*_____   2 ft. FADE IN*
to

End Dupe
E1X 246794
(6)

To {
Scene and Take No. 242-5 CUT 12 Clear Frames
Before Key No. E1X 246 [791]

Scene and Take No. 244-2 CUT 2 Clear Frames
After Key No. X E1X 246 [844]

From {
3 ft. DISSOLVE*   _____ft. FADE OUT*
_____ft. WIPE No.*_____   _____ft. FADE IN*
to

Start Dupe
E1X 246841
End.
E1X 348906
(7)

To {
Scene and Take No. 255-2 CUT 4 Clear Frames
Before Key No. E1X 348 [902]

* Strike out words inapplicable.

Eric Flint _____ Film Editor

OPTICAL SPECIFICATION SHEETS (3)   In this example of a laboratory specification form, only the frames actually appearing in the marked cutting copy (page 97) need to be identified.

103

Methods of Dupe Printing

Black-and-white negative
The standard practice for making a dupe negative is to make as the first stage a master positive on fine-grain positive black-and-white stock. This is sometimes termed a 'fine-grain' or 'lavender', from the colour of the stock used at one time. A further print from this master positive on suitable fine-grain material yields a duplicate negative, whose tonal characteristics can be exactly matched to those of the original. This is the basic 'M & D' (Master and Dupe) sequence.

Colour negative
There are three possible routes available: the standard 'M & D' procedure can be followed by the use of colour intermediate stock, for both stages. A print direct from the colour negative yields a colour intermediate master positive, sometimes known as an 'Inter-pos', and a further print from this on the same stock gives a colour intermediate duplicate negative, or 'Inter-dupe'. The result is a close match to the tonal and colour image of the original negative. An alternative method, expensive but with higher quality of colour reproduction, involved making three separate masters on panchromatic black-and-white stock to represent the single red, green and blue components of the original negative. These were then triple-printed through similar colour filters on to the colour intermediate stock to yield a colour dupe negative. Because of its cost, this system had only limited use and is now restricted to the preparation of protective masters for long term storage.

Colour reversal intermediate
Intermediate stock is now available which allows a duplicate negative to be made at a single step from the original by reversal processing. Such colour reversal intermediates (CRI's for short) very closely match the original for tonal quality and colour rendering and are widely used to make copy negatives for release printing in all film gauges.

Dupes from reversal materials
For reversal originals, both colour and black-and-white, there are two procedures for making duplicates; one is to make a direct reversal duplicate master, giving an image of the same character as the reversal original, with which it can be intercut. The second is to prepare an internegative suitable for printing on to normal positive stocks, and since release prints on regular positive stocks are cheaper than reversal copies, the procedure of converting the whole subject to an internegative including the optical effects is often adopted.

104

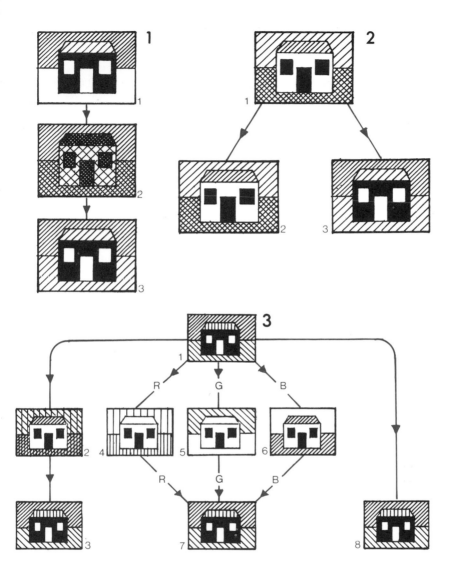

METHODS OF DUPE PRINTING   (1) From a B & W original negative (1) a
Master Positive (2) is printed and a further printing stage from this gives the
Duplicate Negative (3). (2) Reversal originals (1), either colour and B & W, may
be duplicated by printing either an inter-negative (3) or reversal duplicate
master (2). (3) Three methods for duplicating colour negative : through an
intermediate positive (2) to an inter-dupe (3), by way of separation colour
masters (4, 5, 6) which are then triple printed to produce the colour dupe (7), or
direct from the original to a Colour Reversal Intermediate, CRI (8).

Printing Opticals: Masters & Dupes

Master and dupe printing is normally used for effects from black-and-white negatives and often from colour negatives. Direct contact master positives are made from the negative and the optical effects are incorporated when printing the dupe negative.

Fade-out
The dupe is printed on a step printer equipped with shutter which can be opened or closed during printing. For a fade-out, the first section of the dupe is printed with the shutter fully open, the shutter then closes gradually over the required number of frames. This gives decreasing exposure until at the end the shutter is fully closed, the image thus becomes lighter and lighter until only clear film remains. A positive print will thus become darker and darker until it is a uniform black.

Fade-in
When making a fade-in the sequence is reversed, starting with the shutter closed, and opening it up until normal exposure of the dupe is reached at the fade full-in position.

Dissolve
A dissolve effect requires double-printing from two separate master rolls, on the same piece of dupe film. When printing from the master of the first scene (in roll A) the shutter is gradually closed over the length of the mix required. The dupe stock is then rewound and exposed to the second scene (in roll B) while the shutter is gradually opened up. The dupe thus shows a decreasing image of scene 1 superimposed with an increasing image of scene 2 and the print from this dupe shows the first scene gradually dissolving into the second.

Optical printers
Usually, the variable shutter can be set to open or close automatically by means of a cam over a specified number of frames for standard length fades and dissolves. The start of the shutter action must take place at the required frame on the master roll and may be controlled either manually (against a visible frame counter on the printer) in accordance with a cue sheet instruction, or automatically by a pre-set counter. When printing fades or dissolves of non-standard length the printer must be operated manually frame by frame, with the shutter opening set afresh for each exposure. Fades and dissolves from reversal originals on to reversal duplicate masters or internegatives can be made in the same way using the original material instead of the master. Such effects are however often made during the printing of the final copies by A and B printing without the use of duplicate master.

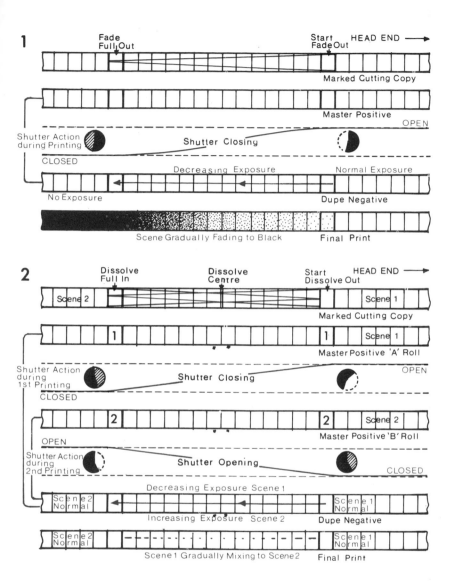

1

Fade Full Out · Start Fade Out · HEAD END →
Marked Cutting Copy

Master Positive · OPEN

Shutter Action during Printing · Shutter Closing

CLOSED

Decreasing Exposure · Normal Exposure

No Exposure · Dupe Negative

Scene Gradually Fading to Black · Final Print

2

Dissolve Full In · Dissolve Centre · Start Dissolve Out · HEAD END →

Scene 2 · Scene 1 · Marked Cutting Copy

1 · 1 · Scene 1 · Master Positive 'A' Roll

Shutter Action during 1st Printing · Shutter Closing · OPEN

CLOSED

2 · 2 · Scene 2 · Master Positive 'B' Roll

OPEN

Shutter Action during 2nd Printing · Shutter Opening · CLOSED

Decreasing Exposure Scene 1

Scene 2 Normal · Scene 1 Normal

Increasing Exposure Scene 2 · Dupe Negative

Scene 2 Normal · Scene 1 Normal

Scene 1 Gradually Mixing to Scene 2 · Final Print

PRINTING OPTICALS: MASTERS AND DUPES   The relation of the marked cutting copy, the corresponding master positives and the printer shutter action while exposing the dupe are shown for a Fade effect (1) and a Dissolve effect (2).

107

Printing Opticals: CRIs

When making dissolve effects on colour reversal intermediate the same procedure is used as for M & D practice except that it is the original negative of the two scenes which is assembled in the A and B printing rolls rather than the master positives.

Fades
When making a CRI fade, however, it is not sufficient merely to print once with a closing shutter, since in the reversal dupe this would give a negative image changing to a uniform black exposure rather than to clear film as required. It is therefore necessary to treat a fade effect as a dissolve to black screen and use the double printing procedure of a mix. In this case the original negative of the scene is made up into the A roll and the B roll consists of cleared negative stock, made by processing unexposed negative film. For a fade-out the picture scene of the A roll is printed on to the CRI stock with a closing shutter action and the CRI is then rewound and exposed to the B roll of clear negative with the shutter opening. The resultant CRI shows the picture image disappearing to clear film, which gives a positive print fading to black.

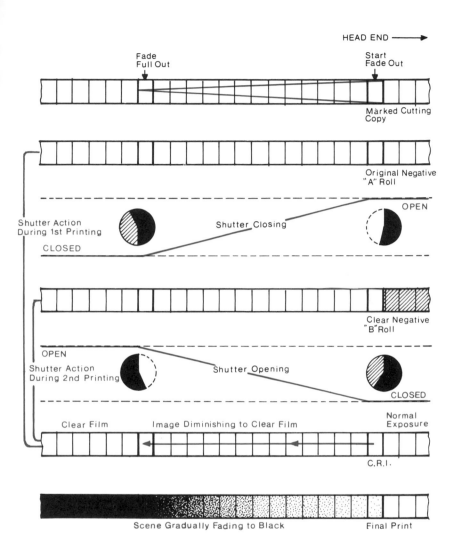

HEAD END ⟶

Fade
Full Out

Start
Fade Out

Marked Cutting
Copy

Original Negative
"A" Roll

Shutter Action
During 1st Printing

Shutter Closing

OPEN

CLOSED

Clear Negative
"B" Roll

OPEN

Shutter Action
During 2nd Printing

Shutter Opening

CLOSED

Clear Film   Image Diminishing to Clear Film

Normal
Exposure

C.R.I.

Scene Gradually Fading to Black   Final Print

PRINTING OPTICALS: REVERSAL INTERMEDIATES When printing directly
from the original negative to produce a CRI dupe, a fade must be treated
as though it were a dissolve to or from a black frame.

109

Printing Opticals: Wipes

At one time it was not unusual for a wipe to or from uniform black screen to be used at the end or beginning of a sequence in much the same way as a fade; iris wipes were often used in this way in black and white films. Now wipes are usually from one scene to another.

Some optical printers are fitted with pairs of blades which can be mechanically moved frame by frame across the printing aperture to produce the wipe, but the effects so obtained are restricted to straight-edge patterns and it is more general now to use a pair of complementary mattes for most forms of wipe.

In a wipe matte, the opaque area changes from frame to frame in accordance with the form of wipe required and when run in one of the paths of an optical printer it allows only a part of the picture to be exposed at each frame.

Straight horizontal wipe
The example shows a simple straight-edge horizontal wipe from right to left. The first scene in the A roll is printed in combination with the A roll wipe matte of the required length, so that a decreasing part of the picture area is exposed in each successive frame. The print stock is then rewound and printed for a second time from the second scene in the B roll together with the matching B roll wipe matte. At this operation, only the previously reserved parts of the frame are exposed so the result shows the area of Scene 1 gradually reducing and being replaced by Scene 2. For a hard edge wipe, the projected image of the matte is focussed sharply on the print stock and for a soft-edge effect the copy lens is slightly defocussed.

The procedure for printing wipes between two scenes is the same for the regular M & D procedure from master positives in the A and B rolls, for CRI printing from the original negative and for reversal originals on to duplicate masters or internegatives.

Since the preparation of a wipe effect is dependent on the availability of a suitable pair of mattes, both the pattern of the wipe required and its length should be checked with the optical department concerned to make sure it can be supplied, since otherwise special mattes will have to be made at considerable expense.

110

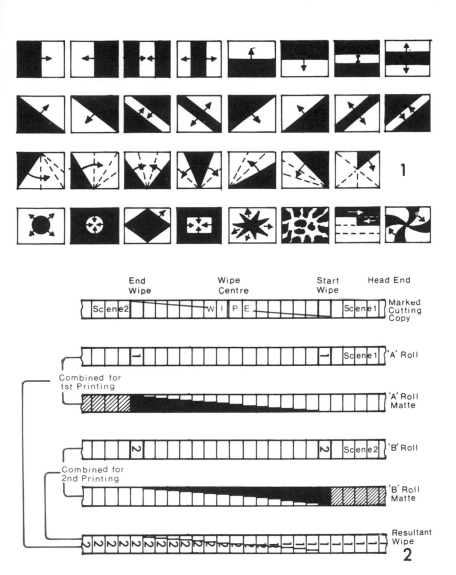

PRINTING OPTICALS : WIPES (1) Varieties of Wipe effects produced by the use of mattes. (2) The make-up of the original scene or master and the corresponding mattes to produce a dupe negative with a wipe effect.

Printing Opticals: Superimposed Titles

Title wording is often superimposed on an action picture, the most popular form being simple white lettering. The original title card showing white letters on a black background should be photographed as a black and white negative, on a high contrast stock. A high contrast master positive is then made from the negative, this shows transparent letters on an opaque backing; it is the title master. A master of the background picture is made in the usual way and the duplicate negative prepared from this is double-printed with the lettering from the title master, so that these appear as black letters over the background negative image. A positive print from this dupe then shows white letters on the picture scene background. When using a colour negative of the picture scene the same procedure is followed using a colour inter-positive as the master and double printing the inter-dupe.

If a colour reversal intermediate is to be made, double-printing it from the title master would produce a *black* title in the final print. If super-imposed white lettering is required, the title negative and the background scene negative must be printed in combination, not successively. The heavy density of the lettering in the title negative then holds back printing, so that after reversal processing the CRI shows the heavy density letters necessary to produce the white title in the print.

Reversal originals
When using a reversal original as the background scene, the reversal duplicate master is double-printed with the title master to give the superimposed white lettering and the same procedure is followed where an internegative is made. In some cases the original white lettered title card may be photographed on a black and white reversal stock to give a title master directly, but this may not give a sufficient density difference between the letters and background.

Successful superimposed titles require careful attention to a number of details:—

(a) Both background scene and title must be photographed with a firmly mounted camera to give steady image position;

(b) White letters should not be superimposed over a high key scene or one with large light areas, where they may become illegible;

(c) Similarly black titles, obtained by double printing the master positive, should not be used over low key scenes or on dark areas;

(d) The exposure of the title negative must be accurate: over-exposure will cause the letters to flare and fine detail to be lost, while under-exposure may allow the background to show through the letters;

(e) In the same way, the double printing of the dupe must be correctly exposed to produce sufficient density in the lettering to obscure the background without any spread or flare around the edges.

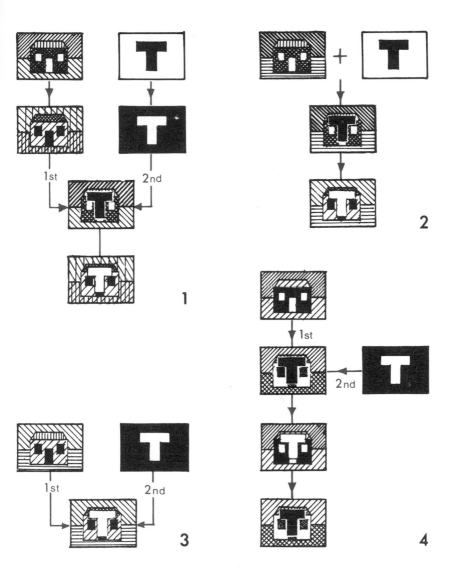

PRINTING OPTICALS : SUPERIMPOSED TITLES (1) In the master-dupe process a white-letter superimposed title is obtained by double-printing the background dupe from a title master. (2) For CRI, the title negative must be optically printed *in combination* with the background negative to produce a dupe negative at one step. (3) White letter titles on reversal are obtained by double-printing with a title master. (4) When black-letter titles are required the master is double-printed and the dupe printed directly from this.

. . . But coloured letters can go anywhere.

Printing Opticals: Colour Letter Titles

Plain white (or black) titles are comparatively simple but sometimes become very difficult to read in certain areas of the background scene, for example, white lettering on a light sky area. Coloured letter titles, often with white or black outlines or shadows, are sometimes preferred, although more complex to prepare.

Such titles are really a special instance of combination printing with mattes and it is essential to obtain a pair of complementary mattes of the overall outline of the letters, one known as the title matte master with a black silhouette on clear background and the other, the title matte, with a clear outline on a black ground.

Making mattes

The title lettering is drawn in colour with all the appropriate shading, and photographed as a normal colour negative against a black background. The title mattes must register exactly with this negative and must therefore be photographed at the same time with the same camera set-up. If the coloured letters are drawn in opaque colours on celluloid sheets, the title matte can be obtained by photographing these cells against an evenly illuminated background using a high contrast black and white stock. The title matte master can then be printed from this. Alternatively white or black letter cards can be prepared by document copying methods to match the coloured lettering and photographed to produce the mattes.

Inter-positive prints are then made from the original negatives of both the background scene and the coloured letter title. The colour inter-dupe is first printed on an optical printer from the background master in combination with the title matte master, which thus reserves the title area unexposed. The inter-dupe is then printed for a second time from the title master combined with the title matte, exposing the dupe only in those areas previously reserved. The resultant dupe negative has the title image on the background scene and a print from this shows the coloured letters superimposed.

The same effect is obtained on a colour reversal intermediate direct from the original negatives of the background and title. In this case it is the background negative which is exposed first in combination with the title matte master (black silhouette) and the second printing is made from the title negative combined with the title matte (clear silhouette) to give the combined dupe at one step.

Coloured letter title effects are not usually attempted using 16mm reversal originals, because of the difficulties in maintaining accurate registration between the components on the 16mm frame.

114

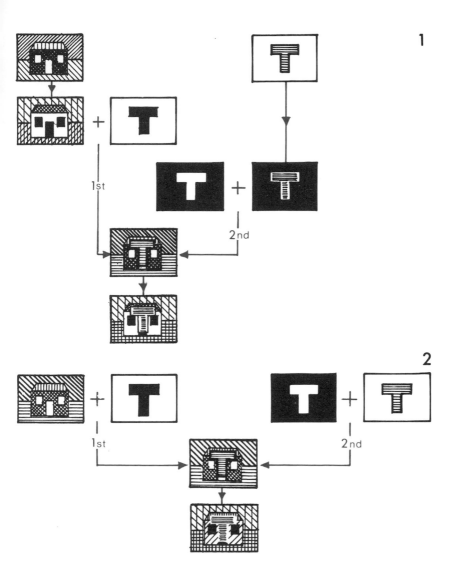

PRINTING OPTICALS: COLOURED LETTER TITLES Coloured letters must be superimposed by the use of a pair of complementary mattes.
(1) For master-dupe process, the dupe is printed first from the Background Master in combination with the Title Matte Master and then double-printed from the Title Master in combination with the Title Matte.
(2) Using CRI, the first printing is from the Background Negative in combination with the Title Matte Master, followed by a second exposure from the Title Negative plus Title Matte.

Title Areas

Titles, captions, etc. must not be placed so close to the edges of the frame that part is cut off on projection. The situation is complicated when a title designed for one format is printed in another. Television use is a particular problem, if its limitations have not been taken into account.

It would be impossible to restrict titles to that area of the frame common to all formats without imposing unacceptable limitations on design, but on the other hand the ideal solution of a new title lay-out for every projection format is economically out of the question. The following guide lines may assist in achieving a satisfactory compromise.

35mm wide-screen prints (1·65–1·85:1)

Although the camera aperture on the negative is 0·868" × 0·631" the area of print for 1·85:1 projection is only 0·825" × 0·446" and no lettering should be positioned too close to these limits to allow for minor variations in projector aperture plates and screen masking. In fact, if all the title is to be safely retained when such a print is used directly for television transmission it would be desirable to restrict the width occupied by lettering to approximately 0·635". This area would also be safely retained when making 16mm prints by reduction from the wide-screen negative.

Anamorphic 35mm

The camera aperture is 0·868" × 0·721" and the projector aperture for 2·35:1 anamorphic projection is 0·836" × 0·700". However, unsqueezed 'flat' prints are often made from anamorphic negatives and it is desirable to retain the title lettering without cut-off in such wide screen prints for an aspect of say 1·75:1. To meet this requirement, the width of titles on the negative should not be greater than approximately 0·612".

35mm film for Television use

Titles and captions must conform to recommended practice, of which the most widely used is the American SMPTE RP.8. From a camera aperture of 0·868" × 0·631" the scanned area for transmission is 0·792" × 0·594" but the safe title area is 0·634" × 0·475" to allow for marginal areas lost on slightly mal-adjusted receivers.

16mm film

Problems of various aspect ratios do not arise, since this gauge is normally shown at AR 1·33:1. The SMPTE recommendation for television practice—photographed area 0·402" × 0·292", scanned area 0·368" × 0·276", safe title area 0·294" × 0·221"—provides the basis for all normal work.

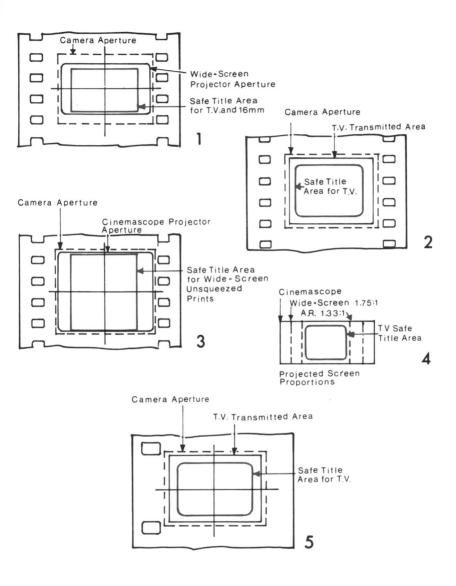

1 — Camera Aperture / Wide-Screen Projector Aperture / Safe Title Area for T.V. and 16mm

2 — Camera Aperture / T.V. Transmitted Area / Safe Title Area for T.V.

3 — Camera Aperture / Cinemascope Projector Aperture / Safe Title Area for Wide-Screen Unsqueezed Prints

4 — Cinemascope Wide-Screen 1.75:1 / A.R. 1.33:1 / TV Safe Title Area / Projected Screen Proportions

5 — Camera Aperture / T.V. Transmitted Area / Safe Title Area for T.V.

TITLE AREAS   To retain 35mm wide screen titles (1) on TV or in 16mm, their width should not exceed the TV Safe Title Area (2). Title width on anamorphic photography must be limited if unsqueezed wide-screen prints are required (3) but to keep them within the TV Safe Area is too great a restriction (4). 16mm photography is generally to A.R. 1·33:1 but titles should be kept within TV Safe Title Area (5).

Photographic Sound Track Transfer

For a number of years after the introduction of sound film, the sound was recorded photographically at the same time that the picture was shot. With the development of magnetic systems for all initial production operations, however, photographic ('optical') processes are now only used in the final step, when a complete sound track is made in preparation for printing composite married copies.

Work of the sound department

In general, three groups of sound components are dealt with separately: 'Dialogue', covering all speech by artists and any commentary, 'Music', the musical background and accompaniment, and 'Effects' both the synchronised sound effects for the action and any general non-sync background noise and 'atmosphere'. All these components are recorded on magnetic striped film which can be run in synchronism wth the picture rush prints. The number of separate sources may be very large, particularly for effects, and pre-mixes of various groups will be made.

When the picture cutting is approved by the director, it is usual nowadays to make a first stage mix of all components on to magnetic film with three stripes, using separate dialogue, music and effects tracks. Subsequently all three are mixed and recorded as the final magnetic master track, containing all components in their correct balance throughout the reel. At the same time, a music and effects (M & E) master may be prepared without the dialogue for later use when making foreign language versions. The final approved master mix is then transferred complete as a photographic recording. Two optical track negatives are sometimes made simultaneously to cover stand-by or export requirements.

Making photographic sound tracks

Almost all photographic tracks are now variable area, in which the sound modulations are represented by the changing width of one or more tracks produced on the film by the movement of the light valve opening. The stock used is a high contrast black and white material, and must be processed in a corresponding high contrast developer.

The density of the exposed negative must be closely controlled and will be specified by the recording studio on the basis of previous experience with the laboratory concerned. A length of uniformly exposed material will normally be supplied at the end of the recorded reel so that the laboratory can process individual tests for each reel before developing the actual track.

Exposed sound negative should be packed exactly as picture negative and clearly labelled with its identity, the type of stock used and the processed density required.

118

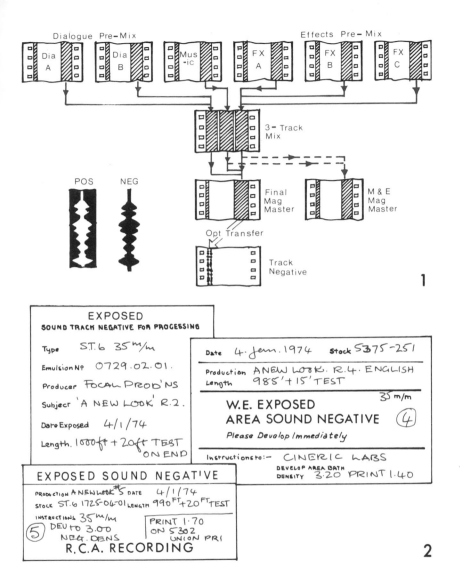

Dialogue Pre–Mix

Dia A — Dia B — Mus-ic — FX A

Effects Pre–Mix

FX B — FX C

3 – Track Mix

POS   NEG

Final Mag Master

M & E Mag Master

Opt Transfer

Track Negative

1

EXPOSED
SOUND TRACK NEGATIVE FOR PROCESSING

Type   ST.6 35 m/m

Emulsion No   0729.02.01.

Producer   FOCAL PROD'NS

Subject   'A NEW LOOK' R.2.

Date Exposed   4/1/74

Length. 1000 ft + 20 ft TEST
ON END

Date 4. Jan. 1974   Stock 5375-251

Production ANEW LOOK. R.4. ENGLISH
Length   985' + 15' TEST

35 m/m

W.E. EXPOSED
AREA SOUND NEGATIVE   ④

Please Develop Immediately

Instructions to:—   CINERIC LABS

DEVELOP AREA BATH
DENSITY 3.20 PRINT 1.40

EXPOSED SOUND NEGATIVE

PRODUCTION A NEW LOOK #5 DATE 4/1/74
STOCK ST.6 1725-06-01 LENGTH 990 FT + 20 FT TEST

INSTRUCTIONS 35 m/m

⑤ DEV to 3.00   PRINT 1.70
NEG. DENS   ON 5302
                 UNION PRI

R.C.A. RECORDING

2

SOUND TRACK TRANSFER   (1) Sound components of Dialogue, Music and Effects are retained as separate magnetic records up to the dubbing of the final master, which is then optically transferred to produce the Sound Track Negative.
(2) Cans of exposed sound negative sent for developing must be clearly labelled with details of the emulsion used and processing required.

Photographic Sound Camera Logs

In the same way that all picture negative sent to the laboratory for processing should be accompanied by a camera log giving detailed instructions, so all sound negatives should be covered by similar reports and orders. However, since sound negatives are now normally recorded as full reels it is not usually necessary to give any instructions for breakdown and make-up for printing, but only whether a given take is to be printed or not. The exact density required in the processed image must also be given, since it may not always appear legibly on the can label, together with the position, length and type of any test sections to be processed separately. The density of the resultant print will usually be specified and sometimes even the particular printing machine to be used will be noted when close technical liaison has been established between the recording studio and the laboratory.

A record of what you want

Again, as with picture material, the sound negative report is the formal order to the laboratory to carry out the specified work and copies will also be sent to the cutting rooms and editor, the production manager and the accounting department for verification of laboratory invoiced charges.

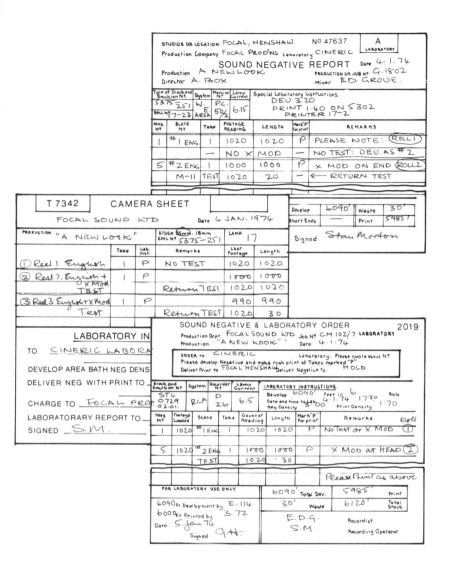

SOUND CAMERA LOGS Details of the sound tracks transferred, density requirements and test details must be included on the Sound Camera Logs giving details to the laboratory.

Photographic Sound Processing

At the laboratory steps must be taken to ensure that the correct density is obtained on the developed sound negative. Although everyone concerned aims at keeping their operations stable, small differences of negative stock sensitivity, variations of recorder lamp current and conditions and changes in developer bath constitution mean that processing conditions must be altered from time to time to give the desired result. Since, with the high contrast materials in use, we are only concerned with one level of density in the negative image, changes of developing time may be regarded as giving changes of resultant density level rather than contrast, and time in the developer solution, usually effected by the speed at which the processing machine is run, is used as the controlling factor.

Density testing
Short sections of the test exposure material at the end of each reel will therefore be removed and processed at different developing times in order to arrive at the actual time required to produce the density specified. For example, if the developing time generally used for a particular stock from a given studio is of the order of 5 minutes on the basis of past experience, two test strips would be developed at 4'30" and 5'30" respectively and the resultant densities measured. The amount of density change for a given time change will have been previously established by the laboratory process control section, so from these tests the actual time necessary for each reel can be estimated. Sample sections of these actual test strips and their density readings are often returned to the sound studio, together with the laboratory report, for confirmation.

Where several reels of a feature film are all recorded at one time, the variations in developing necessary may be found to be quite small; where the studio is satisfied with the consistency both of its own operations and those of the laboratory, the test sections may be omitted on some reels, which will then be given the developing times indicated for the tests on adjacent reels.

After processing the actual track density obtained is measured on each reel, and the negatives made up for rush printing with their appropriate identification. This information will normally be scribed on the film in the unexposed portions at the beginning and end of each roll so that it can be read even when only the track area is printed.

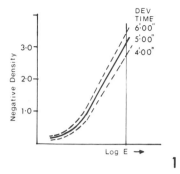

Negative Density
3·0
2·0
1·0

DEV
TIME
6·00"
5·00"
4·00"

Log E →

1

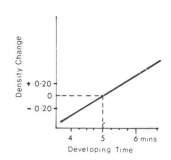

Density Change
+ 0·20
0
- 0·20

4   5   6 mins
Developing Time

2

STUDIO RUSHES — SOUND NEGATIVE REPORT   Date 4 JAN 1974

SUBJECT 'A NEW LOOK'					RECORDING MACHINE NoD 26			AMPS 6·5			NEG STOCK ST6-0729 0201		
					NEGATIVE DENSITY					PRINTING DATA			
Roll No or Indentification Letter	Reel or Scene No.	DEV TEST DATA			35mm INNER Rank 1	35mm OUTER Rank 2		Base Density		Printer	LCP	Print Density	
		Dev Time	Average Density	Actual Dev Time									
1	#1 ENG	No TEST		5'00"	3·02			O·11		A.26	13	1·72	
2	#2 ENG	4'30"	2·85	5'00"	3·00			)		(	)	1·75	1·71
		5'30"	3·15										
3	#3 ENG	4'30"	2·86	5'00"	3·02							1·72	
		5'30"	3·17										
4	#4 ENG	No TEST		5'00'	3·05							1·69	
5	#5 ENG	4'30"	2·89	4'45"	2·98							1·75	
		5'30"	3·20										
6	#6 ENG	4'30"	2·90	4'45"	2·98							1·75	
		5'30"	3·22										

NEG STYLE R.C.A. AREA.	SPECIAL REQUIREMENTS Test + X-Mod to Stan Morton, Focal Sound Ltd, Henshaw.	REQ NEG DENSITY ± 00
		REQ POS DENSITY 1·70

3

SOUND NEGATIVE PROCESSING   Increase of developing time raises the contrast (1) but in variable area tracks can be regarded as increasing the image density (2). The laboratory report (3) records the results of tests developed at varying times together with the densities of ñegative and print finally obtained.

Photographic Sound Printing

Sound negative developing and printing for optimum quality represents one of the most exacting operations in laboratory photographic processing.

Ideally both sound negative and print would have an absolutely sharp and well defined image of high density against a clear background, but some degree of unsharpness is always present as a result of halation and light scatter within the thickness of the emulsion layer. The exposures at recording and printing must be accurately matched so that as far as possible deficiencies in the negative are compensated in the positive.

Overexposure causes the image to spread at its edges; in a high-frequency wave form on a sound track such overexposure will cause the troughs between the modulation peaks to be partially filled in. Underexposure, on the contrary, causes these peaks to be imperfectly formed. Since the peaks of the negative become the troughs of the print and vice versa, positive printing exposure level can compensate somewhat for the effects of negative exposure.

Cross-modulation tests

The optimum print density for any particular negative is determined by making a series of cross-modulations (x-mod) tests. This test consists of a recording combining a middle frequency signal of 6000Hz with a low frequency of 400Hz for 35mm work and 4000/400 for 16mm tracks. In a full test, sections are recorded at different exposure levels so as to provide a range of negative densities after processing.

Each section is then printed at different levels to produce a family of positive prints of differing densities. These are analysed on an optical soundhead, whose output can be measured for the 6000Hz and 400Hz signals separately. The best results are those in which the highest output at 6000Hz is achieved with the minimum 400Hz component and for each negative density there is a positive print density at which this is lowest. The reduction in the 400Hz component level relative to a reference of the same frequency is measured in decibels (−db) and is termed the cancellation. The optimum combination of negative/print densities for the lowest cancellation of all provides the point of aim for the processed negative density and the resultant prints.

The output of the 6000Hz component of a test print is also important, since a loss at this frequency indicates deficiencies of printing machines, either in contact or in film slippage.

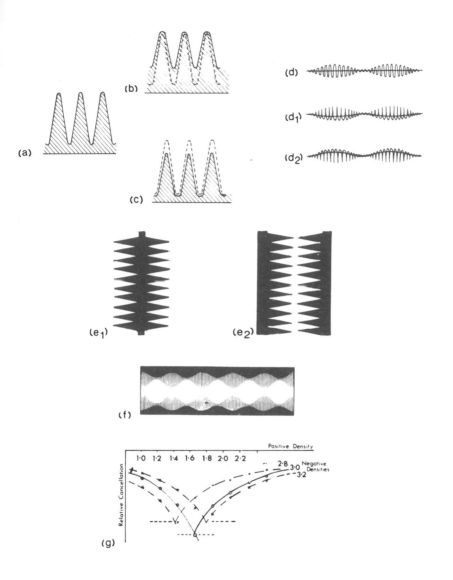

SOUND PRINTING   The correct wave-form of the sound record image (a) may be distorted by over-exposure (b) or under-exposure (c). In a modulated track (d) these distortions can introduce a spurious frequency (d₁ and d₂). Since the peaks of the negative (e₁) become the troughs of the positive print (e₂) and vice-versa, negative exposure and printing exposure must be correctly matched for best results. A cross modulation test (f) is therefore printed at different levels to assess the optimum value.

125

Negative Cutting: Work Prints

With the completion of all editing work and the production of its photographic (optical) sound track, the cutting copies can be handed over for negative matching, cutting and final assembly. The separate work prints of both picture and sound must be checked and identified to make sure that everything is in order and that all the information necessary to guide the negative cutter is clearly shown. Where optical effects have been prepared in advance, the rush prints should have been cut in at their correct positions. However, any effects to be made by direct printing must be clearly marked on the cutting copy.

In addition, there are a number of recognised signs to assist the cutter. These should be shown in yellow grease pencil on the picture work print wherever appropriate:

Jump Cut. Where one or more frames are to be deleted in the middle of a take, the splice in the cutting copy should be marked with a short cross to draw attention to it.

Unintended Splices. At any place the cutting copy has been repaired, the splices should be marked across with a pair of short parallel lines to indicate that no cut is to be made in the negative.

Missing Frames. Frames of the rush prints which have been lost or damaged may be represented by sections of black frame leader, so that the take is 'built-up' to its correct length. This build-up section should be clearly marked to show what it represents. A section in the middle of a take should have a double-headed arrow drawn across it to show that the negative should be continuous. Frames replaced at the end of a cut should be marked with a long arrow, the head of which shows the last frame of the extension. Where build-up leader is put between two different scenes, two arrows are used, with their heads indicating the position of the splice required.

It is sometimes necessary to prepare one or more additional work prints for use in sound dubbing, etc. while the original cutting copy is being used for cutting the picture negative. Several copies may be printed from a 'slash dupe' negative made direct from the cutting copy. Normal black and white positive stock developed to low contrast is used for this purpose. Alternatively, a copy of the work print can be made by printing on to Direct Positive Stock, Type 5360, which yields a positive picture from a positive original by internal reversal when processed in a normal black-and-white developer solution. Good photographic quality is not necessary, but it is essential to print all edge number identification and any other information added by the editor in the cutting room.

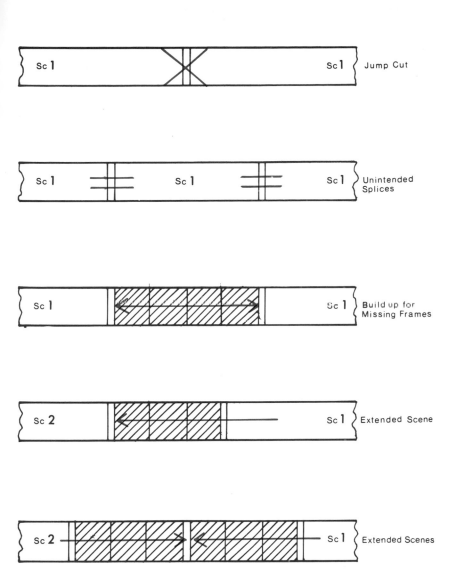

WORK PRINT MARKINGS Conventional markings used on Cutting Copies to assist the cutter.

Picture and Track Synchronisation

During all the stages of editing preparation, the picture work print and the corresponding magnetic sound records have been treated as separate rolls. Only working leader strips are attached at the head ends of each roll, although the standard Academy leader, which has a synchronising start mark 12 feet (in 35mm) ahead of the first picture frame, is often used. Some sound theatres, however, require a longer run-up length of 15 or 18 feet.

The sync-plop

To check the correct relation of separate picture and sound a 'sync-plop' is often cut into the leader of each sound reel. If all preparation stages and machine thread-up are correct, this can be heard when a marked frame in the picture leader is seen. When the Academy leader is used for the picture the plop or buzz is often made to coincide with the last number ('3') shown in the leader 3 feet ahead of the picture but some editors prefer to use a punched hole nearer the picture start.

When the magnetic sound master is finally transferred to a photographic track, the sync-plop will also be recorded and its visible appearance in the photographic sound record provides the basis for the editor to make his final check of synchronisation between picture work print, magnetic master and sound rush print. When this has been confirmed, the sound print must be clearly marked for negative cutting. This is normally shown by a line across the whole width of the print drawn level with the top of the first frame of the picture cutting copy and marked 'picture start—level sync'. This represents the required relation when used on a Moviola or editing table, and therefore is sometimes termed 'edit sync' as well as level or even sync.

Picture and Sound separation

When the picture and sound negatives are printed together on one strip of film to make a married or composite print, the two images are not printed level, but the sound track must be ahead of the picture because of the separation between the picture gate and the optical sound head of the normal motion picture projector. For 35mm copies this advance is standardised at 20 frames and for 16mm at 26 frames.

As a final verification, the tail ends of the picture cutting copy and photographic sound rush print should be correspondingly marked with a line level with the end of the last picture frame and the words 'picture ends—level sync'. A further guide to the laboratory cutter should also appear as another line 20 frames (for 35mm) beyond this last picture frame to indicate where the leader will join at the end of the sound negative when it has been made up for printing with the necessary advance.

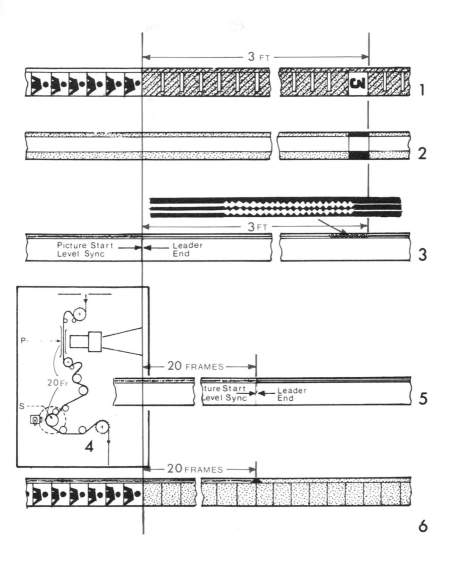

PICTURE AND TRACK SYNCHRONISATION   To check synchronisation
of picture work print (1) and the corresponding magnetic sound (2)
a sound-sync frame is often cut in and recorded, which can be heard when
a marked frame in the leader is seen on projection. The "plop" from this is
recorded when the optical track is transferred (3). In a projector (insert 4)
the sound head S is 20 frames ahead of the picture gate P so the sound in a
composite print must be given the corresponding advance. The track cutting
copy (5) is therefore pulled up relative to the picture in final make-up, so
that in the married print (6) picture and track are in correct relation.

129

Work Prints: Reel Make-up

Editing and preparatory work at the studio is usually in single reels not exceeding some 10½ minutes of projection running time, about 1000 feet of 35mm or 400 feet of 16mm including head and tail leaders. A feature film (of running time say 1 hour 40 minutes), with a 35mm length of 9000 feet, will therefore consist of 10 reels of picture work print, numbered 1 to 10. On exhibition, however, reels longer than 1000 feet are used to minimise the number of projector change-overs during the performance and distribution is now in 'doubled-up' reels up to 2000 feet in 35mm length. The 10 reels of picture work print thus become Parts 1 to 5 and the negative is made up with the identification Parts 1A, 1B, 2A, 2B etc., for joining prints together in double reels before despatch. Editors will therefore find their work print reels 3 and 4 becoming Part 2 in the laboratory, 5 and 6 becoming Part 3 and so on. Where the original work print contains an odd number of reels, the last one, for example Reel 11, would be identified as Part 6AB to indicate that it is complete in itself. When parts are printed as separate A and B reels for subsequent joining, allowance must be made for the track advance being cut off the B reel on assembly. To avoid the loss of sound at this point, the first twenty frames of every even numbered cutting copy reel must be dubbed on to the track of the end of each preceding odd numbered reel as well as at the head end of its own reel.

Printing lengths
Some laboratories now cut the picture negative for printing in the 2000 foot double-reel form, since this avoids splicing subsequent prints. The sound track negatives of the two reels will also be joined at this stage and advanced together. Joins in photographic sound negatives must always be 'blooped' to avoid the lines of the splice causing an objectionable click when the print is projected. This 'bloop' is usually in the form of a small triangular or diamond shaped hole punched out of the negative at the splice; in the resultant print this appears as a black V in the track area which obliterates the join and is almost imperceptible when run on the projector sound system.

Similar considerations apply to 16mm work, especially for television where prints are often joined into a single reel of up to one hour's running time (2160 feet). Editors preparing 16mm sound tracks should therefore check with their laboratory in advance to find out exactly what the final print assembly sequence will be.

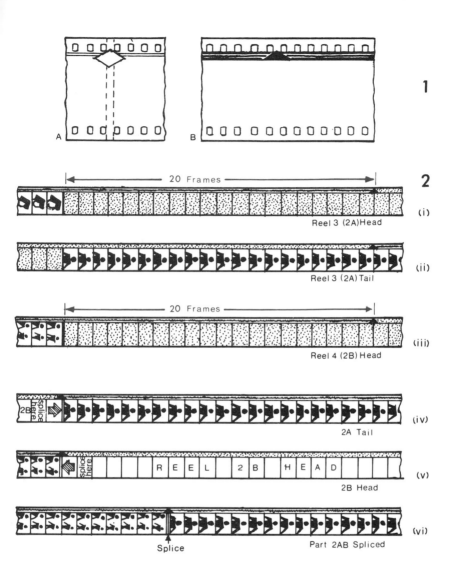

1

2

20 Frames

Reel 3 (2A) Head (i)

Reel 3 (2A) Tail (ii)

20 Frames

Reel 4 (2B) Head (iii)

2A Tail (iv)

R E E L   2 B   H E A D

2B Head (v)

Splice

Part 2AB Spliced (vi)

REEL MAKE-UP   (1) "Bloop" punch at a track negative splice (A) and the resultant print (B).

(2) The advance of the sound track at the head of a reel (i) means that the last 20 frames have no sound track printed alongside (ii). When two reels are joined together for projection the advanced sound at the head of the second part (iii) will be lost unless it is recorded at the end of the preceding reel (iv, v). In this way the two parts can be spliced without loss of sound (vi).

Leaders (1)

Whatever head and tail leaders may have been used on cutting copies during editing stages, a set of one of the standard types must be attached during the final negative cutting operations so that they will be reproduced in all subsequent prints. They have a three-fold purpose:

1. to provide protection against damage during handling and transport to both ends of the roll of film;
2. to identify the subject by its title, part number, language version and other details;
3. at the head end, to indicate the position of the film in the picture gate and sound head for correct projector thread-up and the timing for correct operation.

The protective section of the leader is usually provided by a 6 to 8 foot length of waste raw stock or blank processed film joined on to the beginning and end of the copy but the identification and synchronising sections must be printed from the assembled picture negative. Leaders for sound track negatives are blank throughout the synchronising section, but carry identification wording scribed or printed in the track area to match that of the picture.

Leader patterns

The general form of leader originated by the American Academy of Motion Picture Arts and Sciences in the 1930's is still widely used in general cinematograph practice. After the indentification section giving the subject name and part number, the first part of the synchronising section shows frames marked 'picture start' and '35mm sound start' at a separation of 20 frames, corresponding to the projector picture gate and sound head. From the picture start frame to the first frame of the picture is a distance of 192 frames (12 feet in 35mm), printed as opaque black except for a series of clear frames with black numbers 11 to 3 at 16 frame intervals. Symbols to represent the sound head thread-up frame corresponding to these numbers appear 20 frames in advance of each. The last 47 frames of the leader immediately preceding the first picture are printed in black throughout.

At the tail end of a B reel, the last picture is followed by 48 black frames, known as the run-out leader, after which comes the final part title and identification. The tail end of an A reel and the head end of a B reel if printed separately carry frames marked 'splice here' to indicate where the two sections are to be joined for final projection.

Since 16mm prints are often made by direct reduction from a 35mm original, some forms of leader carry synchronising frames marked for both 35mm sound at 20 frames advance and 16mm sound at 26 frames advance from the standard picture start frame but 16mm practice is otherwise identical.

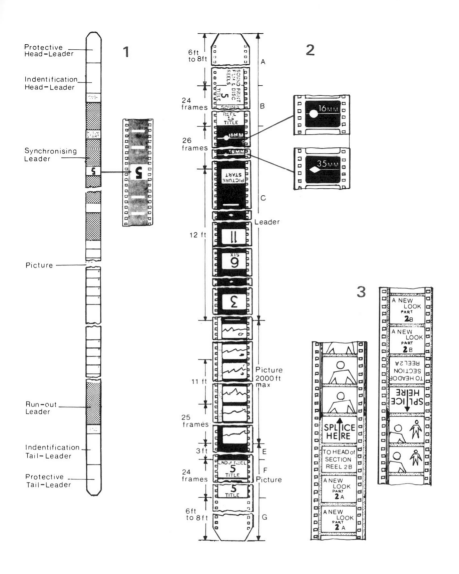

LEADERS (1) The essential features of head and tail leaders.
(2) Details of the standard Academy Leader make-up.
(3) When reels are printed separately for joining later, the tail end leader of
the first part and the head leader of the second are marked to show the point
at which they are to be spliced for projection.

Leaders (2)

SMPTE Leader

Although well established in regular motion picture projection practice, the Academy leader was not considered to provide sufficient accuracy of timing for television operation and the appearance of single clear frames of numerals in otherwise black material was found distracting. In 1965 the Society of Motion Picture and Television Engineers (SMPTE) therefore introduced a new pattern of leader to improve these points and it was hoped that this type would become universal for both theatrical and television practice. This leader introduced a number of new features especially in the synchronising section.

The synchronising numbers are now shown in every frame from the Picture Start up to the final run-in 47 frames, each number from 8 to 3 appearing as a black figure on a medium density background for a length of 24 frames, or one second's duration at 24 p.p.s. As an aid to accurately timed operations, a radial line rotates over the background once every second while each number appears, showing a change of background density as it moves. The last frame of the count-down numerals, two seconds before the first picture frame, shows the figure '2' and is followed by 47 frames of uniform density but not opaque black. At the tail end, the run-out section immediately after the last picture is extended to 87 frames of similar uniform low density.

Frames showing 35mm and 16mm photographic sound head positions relative to the picture start frame are included, and in addition frames in the numbered section are identified 'M 70' and 'M 35' to indicate the magnetic sound start positions for 70mm and 35mm prints.

EBU Leader

A somewhat similar overall approach for a universal leader has been proposed by the European Broadcasting Union (EBU); as in the SMPTE version the count-down numbers in the synchronising section are displayed for one second (24 frames) each and a small clock pointer rotates around the number once a second. The picture start frame is shown 144 frames (6 seconds) ahead of the first picture frame, but the full leader covers a total of 10 seconds numbered count-down frames for dubbing and other requirements. 35 and 16 optical and magnetic sound sync. frames are shown for the picture start position only.

Although widely used for television film purposes neither of these leaders can be regarded as effectively 'universal' for all motion picture use and specific instructions must be given to the laboratory or negative cutters whenever any particular type of leader is definitely required.

 1

 2

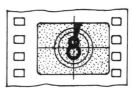

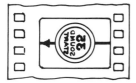

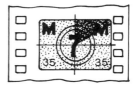

 3

LEADERS FOR TELEVISION (1) Earlier type of leader for TV prints (1958).
(2) The SMPTE Universal Leader, in which a radial line rotates once every
second to allow accurate timing in transmission.
(3) Rotating index mark in proposed E.B.U. Leader.

Cue Marks

Associated with the specification of head and tail leaders is the provision of cue marks in each print. When running a number of reels in sequence on two projection machines, it is necessary to change over from the end of one reel to the beginning of the next as imperceptibly as possible without any pause or interruption of the action. Cue marks to assist these change-overs are therefore printed at two positions towards the end of each complete reel. The first of these occurs seven seconds, 168 frames, ahead of the second, which itself is one second from the last picture frame and the beginning of the run-out black leader.

The appearance of the first cue mark, known as the motor cue, is a warning to the projectionist to start the second projection machine running so that it is completely up to speed by the time the second cue mark, known as the change-over cue, is seen. At this moment the projectionist operates the change-over switch to close a shutter in front of the first projector and open one in front of the second, so that the new reel is seen on the screen. The same action also switches the sound from one machine to the other.

The distance from the motor cue to the end of the outgoing reel is similar to that from the picture start frame to the first picture on the incoming reel. However on the basis of his own experience of the length of time taken for a particular machine to get up to speed, the projectionist may thread-up on a later number of the head leader so as to obtain a precise change-over even with a slow-starting projector. Small differences in the specified positions for cue marks between the Academy and SMPTE Universal standards should be noted.

Form of cue marks

In British and American practice each set of cue marks appears over four consecutive frames in the upper right hand corner of the picture in the form of circular dots but in France and some other European countries the motor cue is a square and the change-over a circle. The size of these cue dots is specified by the published standards of each country, as well as their location within the frame. SMPTE gives different positions for anamorphic and flat wide-screen release prints to ensure best visibility under varied projection conditions.

Cue marks on the print are generally obtained by physically punching a hole out of the negative, or scribing a circle on its emulsion surface. As this is an irretrievable operation, it is generally not undertaken by the laboratory until it is absolutely certain that there is no possibility of recutting involving the last scenes of the reel. In fact, it may be considered undesirable ever to cue-mark the original negative itself and to punch only duplicate negatives or intermediates made for general release printing. In any case the editor should give formal instructions to the laboratory that the negative may be cue'd.

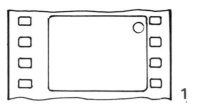

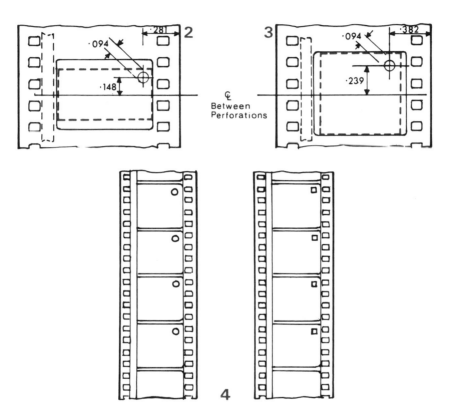

CUE MARKS (1) Projector change-over cue marks appear in the upper right-hand corner of the frame near the end of the reel.
(2) Cue mark location for wide-screen pictures.
(3) Cue mark location for anamorphic pictures.
(4) In some European countries the final change-over cue is shown as a square dot.

Negative Selection for Cutting

When the completed cutting copies have been received from the editor, the laboratory's first operation is to identify and bring together all the negative scenes and takes involved, usually reel by reel. The edge numbers of the rush print normally provide the necessary information, although some editors add their own coding marks in the perforation area of the rush print to identify the scene and take numbers directly. An explanation of a code system used in this way can be very helpful to the laboratory negative cutter.

The cutting log

The scene identification starts by listing the first and last complete edge numbers which appear in each cut appearing in the work print in order; where a cut is so short that it misses the edge numbers appearing every 16 frames, the editor should make sure that identification is given by scribing the nearest edge number plus or minus the appropriate number of frames at some convenient point, otherwise the cutter has no guide at all of the material to be used.

The cutting log sheet should also show the scene and take number from which each cut has been taken, either by the editor's edge coding or from the previously completed negative records. From these records the original daily roll number and location of the negative, in its breakdown storage can, can also be noted.

At this stage it is a help to the negative cutter to note wherever the same scene is used in two or more separate cuts in the work print. Such cross-cut references may either be noted as the additional cut numbers in the continuity or indicated by identifying crosses or ticks against both cuts. This draws attention to the fact that when the first cut section has been used, the remaining part must be held ready for further use later in the reel. Particular attention must be paid to this point when the later use of the scene occurs in a different reel.

When the cutting log sheet is finished for a complete reel, or preferably a series of reels, the negative of the identified scenes and takes, including opticals and special effects, must be selected from the breakdown cans where it has been stored, and brought together in preparation for actual cutting. With 35mm film the individual scenes and takes will usually be spooled on separate cores with protective spacing and labels, so that the handling of the chosen material is simple.

In 16mm practice, however, there is a general tendency to keep the original material in its initial daily rolls and not to break it down for storage because of the danger of damage during additional handling. In this case all the daily rolls involved in a particular work print are brought together and held in this form until cutting begins.

138

NEGATIVE CUTTING DEPT.

PRODUCTION A NEW LOOK R.2. PICTURE

	Key Numbers	Scene & Take No	Tin Numbers
	HEAD LEADER		
E2x993	484 — 490	207-2 X	152
	561 — 570	208-2	152
	496 — 502	207-2 X	152
	610 — 621	209-3 XX	152
	529 — 540	207-3	152
	630 — 636	209-3 XX	152
	654 — 661	210-1 ✓	152
	485 — 691	211-1	202
	662 — 668	210-1 ✓	152
	721 — 730	211-2	202
6x1042	101 — 103	F.O. OPT 5	214
" "	104 — 1		
E1x 246	793 —		
	937 —		

CUTTING LOG SHEET

COMPANY FOCAL PROD'NS   PRODUCTION A NEW LOOK

DATE 7 JAN 1974   REEL 2   SHEET

Scene No.	Key Numbers ·· From	To	Uncut Can No.	Roll No.	Take No.	Slate No.	Grading Y	M	C
1	E2x993434	490	152	17604	2	207			
2	561	570	152	17604	2	208			
3	496	502	152	17604	2	207			
4	610	621	152	17604	3	209			
5	529	540	152	17604	3	207			
6	630	636	152	11604	3	207			

SUBJECT A NEW LOOK.   VERSION DOM.   TYPE OF PHOTOGRAPHY W/S

REEL No 2   TYPE OF NEGATIVE E/C 5254   PROD No 31078

Negative Key Nos	Scene & Take	Daily Roll No	Edge No Finish	Footage	Cross Cut Ref:	Description of Scene	Light Change No	R	G	B
						Identification header	1			
						Control Chart	2			
						Head Leader	3			
E2x 993 484	207-2	17604	490			Man and Woman M.L.S.	4			
E2x 993 561	208-2					Man by Window M.S.	5			
E2x 993 496	207-2				4C 4	Man & Women M.L.S.	6			
E2x 993 610	209-3					Man . C.U.	7			
E2x 993 529	207-3					Man & Woman M.L.S	8			
E2x 993 630	209-3				4C7	Man C.U.	9			
E2x 993 654	210-1					Woman in Chair M.S.	10			
E2x 993 685	211-1					Woman C.S.	11			
E2x 993 662	210-1				4C10	Woman in Chair. M.S.	12			
E2x 993 721	211-2					Woman. C.S.	13			
6x1042 101	Opt. 5					" " F.O.	14			
6x1042 104	Opt. 6					F.I. House. Ext L.S.	15			
E1x 246 793	242-5					" " " "	16			
E1x 246 937	243-2					Man to House M.L.S	17			
E1x 246 830	244-1					Man at Door	18			
6x 1042 110	Opt. 7					Dissolve to Man in Room	19			
E1x 246 850	243-1					Woman Enters. C.U	20			
E1x 246 991	361-4					...	2.			

NEGATIVE SELECTION FOR CUTTING Cutting log sheets giving key numbers are prepared from the work print to identify scene and take and the negative storage location.

Cutting Picture & Track Negatives

This is a critical operation in the laboratory sequence: negative cutting is a key job to be done by specialists under optimum conditions for clean and safe film handling.

The original negative of all the individual scenes and takes listed are arranged in order, together with negative of the standard leader and the appropriate part titles. The cutting copy is located on one path of a synchroniser and the first picture scene matched to it by edge numbers; when correct synchronisation has been confirmed the negative is actually cut through the centre of the frame preceding the first splice to the head leader and the unwanted portion ahead of the section used spooled up separately. The first scene negative is then joined to the leader and both negative and cutting copy wound on through the synchroniser until the end of the first scene is reached. After checking the match of work print and negative the latter is now cut through the centre of the frame following the splice and the remaining unwanted portion of the negative spooled up with the first section for storage as 'trims'.

This procedure of synchronising, checking and cutting the negative to match the cutting copy scene is repeated throughout the whole reel until it is completed with the addition of the tail leader and part titles. Each cut section is preferably joined up as the reel progresses by working at a cutting table with a splicing machine, as this reduces the handling.

Adding printer cues

As the final step, the picture negative must now be cued to allow the changes in printing level for each cut to take place at the correct point. One method is to cut a shallow notch from the edge of the film outside the perforations, which is detected on the printer by a lightly-weighted roller operating a micro-switch relay. Another system, which does not involve cutting and possibly weakening the edge, is to apply small patches of metallic foil in the film margin. The passage of these past a high frequency proximity detector similarly operates the light change mechanism through a relay.

Cutting sound track negatives is comparatively simple, since normally each reel consists of a single continuous take from the transfer operation. It is therefore only necessary to add head and tail leaders with their information sections and printer start marks to match the work print, blooping the splices at both ends as previously described.

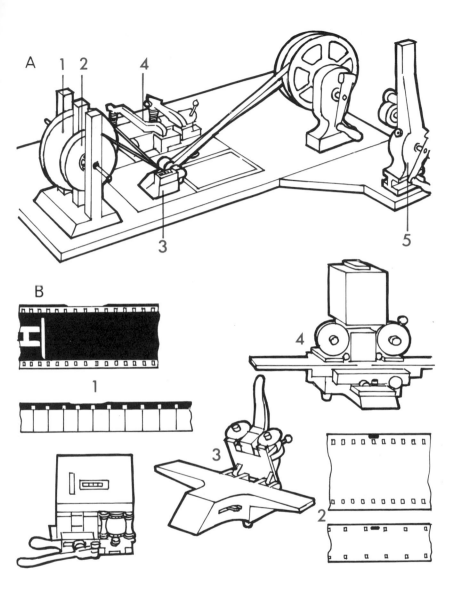

CUTTING PICTURE NEGATIVE (A) Cutting Table. The Picture negative 2 is matched to the cutting copy 1 through a two-way synchroniser 3, cut and joined using the splicer 4. Unused sections of negative ("trims") are wound on cores on the tight-wind 5. (B) Light Change Cues. Notches (1) can be cut in the edge of 35 or 16mm picture negative or metallic patches (2) can be attached by either a manual (3) or automatic applicator (4)

A & B Cutting

For many years, practically all 16mm original photography was undertaken on reversal materials and the most economical method of obtaining fade and dissolve effects as well as simple white-letter super-imposed titles was to assemble the whole reel in A and B rolls and make all positive copies by double printing using a fade shutter on the printer. The general procedure is similar to that described for printing optical effects, but instead of only the scenes involved in the fade or dissolve being prepared in this way, all scenes of the complete reel are cut into one or other of the A and B rolls, the sequence changing from one roll to the next only at an effect. Scenes involved in dissolves must of course be overlapped by the appropriate length to allow superimposed double-printing during the shutter opening or closing action.

First example

The first effect is a fade-out at the end of Sc.15, so all scenes up to this point appear in the A roll. Scene 16 starts with a fade-in so this scene is made up in the B roll, and is followed by Scenes 17 and 18. Scene 18 however mixes to Scene 19, so that Scene 19 is in the A roll, where it is followed by Scene 20, and so on. Both rolls are made up to exactly the same length with black leader, in the A roll between the end of Scene 15 and the start of the dissolve-in of Scene 19 and in the B roll before the start of Scene 16 and after the end of the dissolve-out of Scene 18.

Second example

The titles to be superimposed by double-printing the first scene are assembled in the B roll, while Scene 1 itself is in the A roll, with black spacing to correspond.

Cutting and make-up must be done on a multi-way synchroniser with paths for the cutting copy and the separate A and B rolls. In some cases it may be necessary to have an additional C roll for title or other superimpositions.

Care must be taken to use first class quality black leader for all spacing between original scenes. A minimum density of 3·0 is recommended and can be obtained by developing white-lighted or fully exposed positive stock in a positive developer bath. The perforation holes of the spacing must correspond to those of the original picture material on each side: double perforated where the original is double, single where it is single. Make sure that single perforated leader has its holes on the same edge as those of the original. All splices must be carefully made, correctly aligned and not too deeply scraped. Fresh cement must always be used, with only the minimum amount to avoid wet splices marking the next layer of film when winding up.

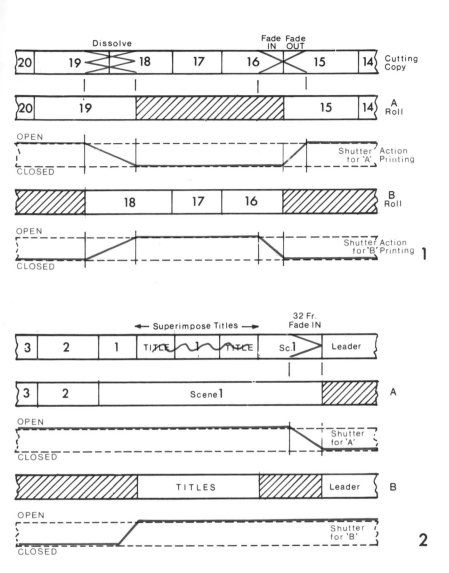

A & B CUTTING Examples of A and B roll assembly and printer shutter action for fades and dissolves (1) and for superimposed titles (2).

Checker-Board Cutting

An extension of the A and B roll concept allows invisible splices to be made between scenes of 16mm material. An ordinary overlap cement splice, even if made as narrow as is safe and cut through the centre of a perforation hole, will appear within the picture area of an adjacent frame in a very obvious way and can be most objectionable.

However, if A and B rolls in which each scene alternates with black spacing are used, splices can be made in such a way that the overlap is always hidden by the opaque leader and is never visible in the resultant print. The rule to remember is that it is always the picture original that is overlapped and scraped on making a splice, never the black spacing. It will be seen that in order to maintain this condition at both ends of a scene, it is necessary to turn the scene around in the splicer when coming to the tail end join to make sure that it is correctly scraped in both positions. This operation may seem rather complicated, especially on certain splicing machines, when using film perforated on one edge only, and the less experienced cutter should practice thoroughly with waste material until the procedure is familiar. Some manufacturers are now producing twin splicers with double cutting and scraping positions to allow assembly in this way without turning the film over.

Splices

In any case, all splices must be made on a correctly aligned splicer and must be carefully checked to ensure that the width of the overlap cut and the width of the scraped portion are exactly matched. In splicing reversal originals there should be no transparent clear line of scrape visible beyond the edge of the black spacing. Similarly, with 16mm negatives, the edge of the black spacing must not overlap into the adjacent picture area.

This method of alternating scene with black leader throughout both A and B rolls is termed 'checker-board' cutting. The example shows the sequence of scenes with fade-out, fade-in and dissolve previously chosen to illustrate regular A and B assembly, with which it should be compared.

144

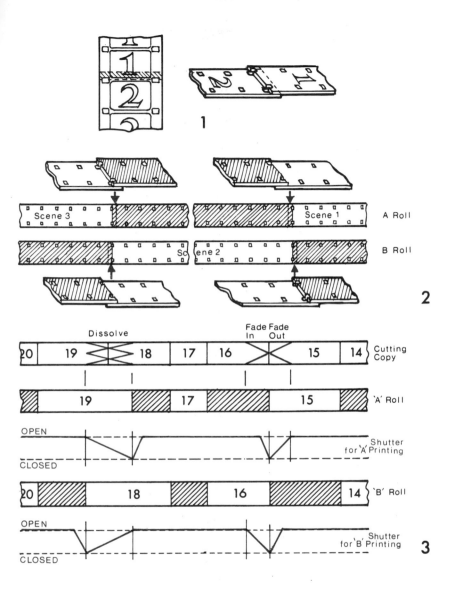

CHECKER-BOARD CUTTING   Normal overlap splices between scenes (1) show appreciably in the 16mm picture area. By cutting alternate scenes with black leader in A and B rolls (2) the splice overlap can be hidden. The example (3) shows checker-board assembly of scenes for fade and dissolve printing.

Zero Cut & Auto-Opticals

Another method of making the splices between scenes invisible is to use a printer fitted with a very fast operating supplementary shutter, known as a zero-cut shutter, which can be cued to open and close at the beginning and end of each scene when printing from A and B rolls cut over-length in checker-board fashion.

Since, when printing at high speeds, the shutter action is not instantaneous, all scenes in the A and B rolls should be extended by two frames at their head and tail ends to provide a four-frame overlap. The scenes in each roll alternate with black leader, as in checker-board cutting, but normal splice overlaps can be used since they occur outside the printed section. In practice, there is usually a slight double-printed effect for one frame at each scene change as a result of the action of the zero-cut shutter.

Zero-cut printers are not available at all laboratories, so it is necessary to check with the laboratory concerned before finally deciding to make up original material in this form.

Auto-opticals

When an intermediate, such as a colour internegative or CRI, is to be made optically from the original for release printing purposes, other procedures may be adopted for invisible splices and fade and dissolve effects. Technicolor's Auto-splice Deletion and Auto-optical methods are examples of such systems.

In Auto-splice Deletion, the original material (usually a 16mm colour negative), is made up in one roll and spliced normally but each scene is cut one frame over-length at the beginning and end. When printing the derivative colour reversal intermediate from this roll the optical printer is programmed to skip the two surplus frames at each splice, so that the resultant print is of correct length.

A somewhat similar procedure is used when making dissolves by Auto-optical printing. Here again the original is assembled in one roll, not as A and B, but a suitable length of spacing is cut in between the two scenes to be mixed. After the variable opening shutter of the optical printer has closed down at the end of the dissolve-out of the first scene, the printer mechanism is programmed to rewind the stock in the camera head while the spacing section is running through the projector head. As the second scene comes up, the camera head starts to run forward again and the variable shutter opens up to expose the second scene superimposed on the first with a dissolve effect.

Procedures of this type involve optical printers with sophisticated pre-set programme control and negative cutting in this form is generally restricted to Technicolor's laboratories, where it is used for 16mm work and for half-frame Techniscope negatives.

146

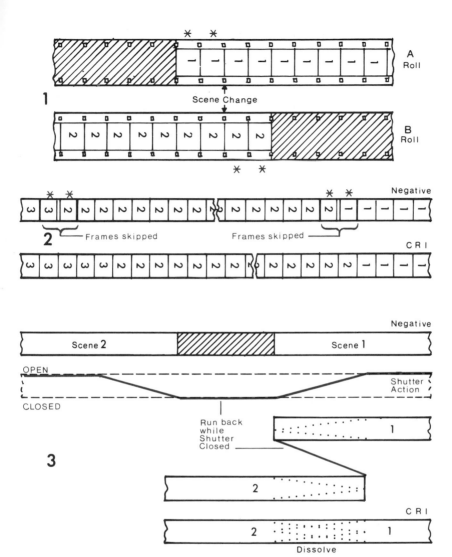

ZERO-CUT AND AUTO-OPTICALS   (1) For invisible splices by zero-cut printing the scenes are assembled two frames overlength in A and B checker-board rolls with a total four-frame overlap at scene changes.
(2) In Auto-Splice Deletion the scenes are cut one frame overlength at each end in a single roll, the extra two frames at each scene change being skipped during printing on an optical printer.
(3) Auto-optical printing allows dissolve and fade effects to be printed from a single roll by automatic rewinding during optical printing.

147

Limitations of A & B Cutting

Length of effects
Although checker-board cutting can now be generally accepted, not all printers can provide a full range of lengths for fades and dissolves on their shutter mechanisms. 48 frame effects are generally accepted as standard, but if other lengths are required the laboratory should be consulted to confirm their availability.

Length of scenes
There are often limitations on the length of individual scenes and on the space required between two consecutive effects. In general, no single scene should be less than 8 frames in length in 35mm or 18 frames in 16mm, or the light change mechanism may not have time to re-set itself between successive scenes.

Proximity of effects
Where a dissolve effect follows a scene change in a checker-board cut roll it is usually recommended that the black spacing section should not be less than 54 frames to allow the fade shutter time to re-set itself over the normal cycle of 48 frames plus a safety margin of 6 frames.

Similarly, where a dissolve-out or fade-out follows directly on a dissolve-in or fade-in in the same scene, few frames should be allowed between the end of one shutter action and the beginning of the next; a minimum of 12 frames at such a position is recommended. When the fade-out of one scene is immediately followed by the fade-in of another, some laboratories prefer 8 or 16 frames of black between the last fade-full-out frame of one and the first start-fade-in of the next.

A and B cutting, although originally used for 16mm reversal, is now sometimes used for 35mm negatives, especially where intermediates are to be prepared. The procedures for negative cutting in both 35 and 16 are generally similar to those already described, but it should be remembered that for positive prints or CRI's fades from negative A and B rolls should be treated as the scene dissolving to or from black screen so that the other portion is represented by *clear* negative spacing. A fade-out followed by a fade-in can thus be handled with both the two picture scenes in one roll and the clear negative in the other.

Where A and B rolls are assembled outside and sent to the laboratory for printing, it is essential that detailed instructions for all effects should be sent, preferably in the form of a footage cue sheet measured from the start mark of the leader, together with a fully marked-up cutting copy. The length and type of each effect must be specified but no markings should ever be made on the picture area of the original material itself.

148

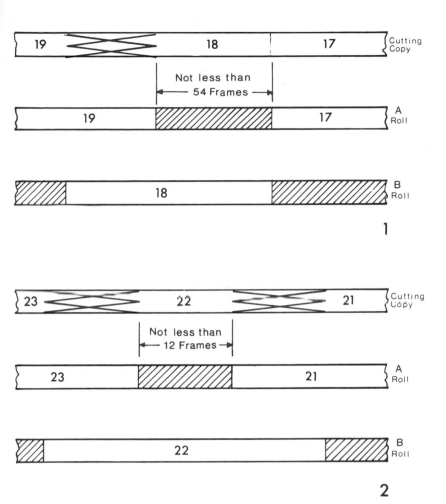

A AND B LIMITATIONS   To allow time for re-setting the printer shutter the start of a dissolve effect should not be closer than 54 frames to the preceding scene change (1) and there should be at least 12 frames between the end of one dissolve and the beginning of the next (2).

Negative Cleaning

The greatest care must be taken to avoid dirt at all stages of negative cutting:

Keep all work places and bench surfaces really clean;

Wear clean lint-free cotton gloves;

Clean from your splicer all scrapings, chips and dried cement at frequent intervals;

Do not leave rolls of film awaiting work where they can collect dust: keep them in their cans (even black leader);

Keep your rewinders and synchronisers in good condition so that there is no danger of their straining or distorting the film;

Keep grease pencils, sticky tape, pencil sharpenings (and cigarette ash!) out of the cutting room, not just away from the work bench;

Beware of wet splices;

Wind film carefully—not so loosely that adjacent turns can cinch nor so tightly that dirt or dust is ground in.

Keep the ends of rolls off the floor!

Following negative cutting is the vitally important but often overlooked step of negative cleaning before printing. The cut rolls have undergone their maximum exposure to the hazards of film handling on the cutting bench and splicer and any loose dust particles which may have been picked up in the process must now be removed before they become too firmly attached or embedded in the emulsion surface.

Cleaning methods

At the laboratory all cut reels should be cleaned immediately after assembly to remove splicer debris and loose particles. In the hands of a skilled operator this can be satisfactorily done using cleaned and brushed velvet pads, if necessary with a proprietary cleaning solvent, but automatic wet cleaning machines, enclosed to prevent the escape of solvent vapours, are now widely used in larger establishments. Among these are machines with rotating camel-hair brushes or replaceable cleaning pads, but perhaps the best known are the ultra-sonic cleaning machines, in which high frequency vibrations are applied to the film as it passes through a solvent liquid bath to remove firmly attached particles.

Remember, however, that even ultra-sonic cleaners cannot remove scratches and abrasions of the film surface: to cure these, wet-gate printing may be necessary. Equally, wet-gate printing will not cover up embedded dirt particles which will still appear on the resultant print. The only safe approach is to avoid causing defects at all stages of handling, not to rely on their subsequent cure.

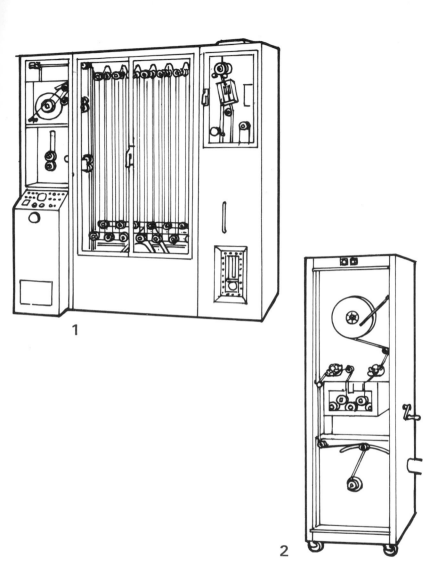

1

2

NEGATIVE CLEANING MACHINES (1) High-speed Ultra-sonic cleaning machine. (2) Solvent cleaner with velvet-covered scrubbing rollers.

Protective Facilities

At this point the whole of the production investment is concentrated into the few rolls of cut assembled original material and the possibility of serious damage at subsequent stages, although remote, cannot be neglected. A measure of protection can be provided by preparing facilities from which a copy negative could be made should a disaster occur. Such facilities are termed protective masters or protection prints.

Black-and-white
For black and white picture negative, these consist of a fine-grain black and white master positive print made from the complete cut negative on to the appropriate stock. From this master positive a duplicate negative can be made either of the whole reel or of any portion of it which has been damaged.

Colour
With colour negatives there are several possibilities. A colour intermediate master positive may be made and held in case of need, when a corresponding colour intermediate dupe negative can be produced from it. Alternatively, a colour reversal intermediate (CRI) dupe can be made directly from the original and held until wanted.

Unfortunately, neither of these provide permanent long term protection, since both are liable to fade with age in the same way as the original colour negative. For long period 'archival' protection the only permanent (but expensive) method is the preparation of a set of three colour separation master positives on black and white panchromatic stock.

Protection for 16mm colour reversal originals can be provided in the form of a copy reversal master, but where an internegative is made for subsequent release printing the original reversal can be retained without further use and serves itself as protection.

To obtain optimum quality in any protective picture material the major variations in the original camera exposure must be corrected as far as possible. They should therefore be printed with scene-to-scene grading corrections whenever possible, rather than at a single print exposure level throughout (one-light printing).

Protective prints are not usually made from photographic sound negatives, since the original magnetic master of the final mixing will normally be available for re-recording in the event of damage. All protective materials should be packed in sealed cans and stored under the best possible conditions of low and uniform temperature and humidity. It is sometimes a requirement of production insurance that they must be stored in a different building or at the insurer's instructions.

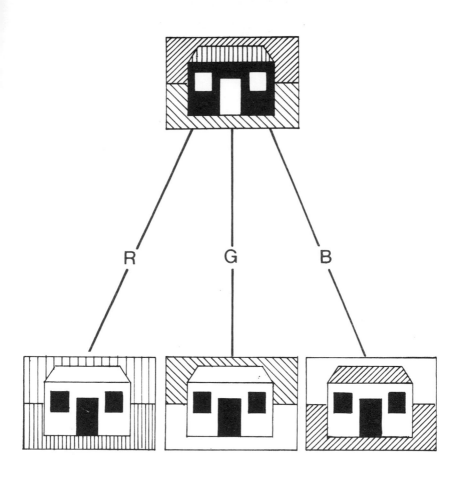

PROTECTIVE FACILITIES For complete archival protection a set of three colour separation master positives are printed from the original colour negative.

Grading for the Answer Print (1)

The preparation of the answer print from the finally cut negative is perhaps the most critical of all laboratory operations. It is the stage at which the visually creative efforts of the whole production team are brought to realisation.

Communication with the grader

Although comments on the character of the rush prints will have been passed back to the laboratory by the contact man during production shooting, there are often changes of mind when all scenes are finally viewed in sequence in the work print. At this stage, especially if 'one-light' rushes have been supplied, the grader should watch a cutting copy show with the director and cameraman, who should detail their intentions. The grader should make extensive notes as to the way in which the scenes of the cutting copy must be corrected to give the right impression, remembering that, in practice, his freedom of action is limited to increasing or reducing the printing levels of the yellow, cyan and magenta components of each individual scene. It is always of great assistance to the grader if the production team can agree on specific scenes in a cutting copy to be taken as satisfactory guides for selected sequences.

Grading is in fact one of the few laboratory operations where personal subjective judgements are of primary importance and the skilled grader must be able to interpret the cameraman's comments 'the night sequence in reel 3 is all a little too dark and too warm' into the terms 'Reel 3, scenes 73–85, correct minus 1 point density, minus 1 point red'.

Applying corrections

Armed with the production crews' comments, the grader can then record the estimated corrections. If all the prints used were supplied as one-light rushes, these corrections can be applied to the standard one-light printing level to give the printer point settings for each scene. However, where graded rushes were supplied or where the original rush print data is not readily available, it may be more convenient to re-assess the whole series of scenes in the cut negative reel on a colour analyser using the cutting copy, with its appropriate scene-by-scene ratings, as a reference. Colour analysers may be fitted with a still projector to show a single frame of a cutting copy scene side-by-side with the colour monitor so that the grader can adjust his controls to match the two, with the necessary allowance for the correction considered necessary from the cutting copy viewing.

By such methods, a first set of printer point values for each scene of the cut negative is obtained and converted into the punched paper tape coding used to operate the light mechanism of the printer.

154

1

TIMING RECORD

DATE 9. Jan 74

SUBJECT A NEW LOOK VERSION DOM.
REEL N° 2 TIMINGS N° 1 RUN N°
N° GRADER 369 CORR. BY

2

L C P	Y	C	M	CORRECTION	L C P	Y	C	M		L C P	Y	C	M	CORRECTION
1	20	20	20		35					69				
2	24	25	25	(Chart)	36					70				
3	20	20	20		37					71				
4	26	20	28		38					72				
5	26	20	28											
6	26	20	28											
7	27	21	29											
8	26	20	28											
9														

COLOUR TIMING RECORD

CARD N° 1

TITLE A NEW LOOK CLIENT FOCAL PRODUS DATE 9.1.74
REEL 2

	Footage	SCENE DESCRIPTION	EFFX	Y	M	C	Correction	Y	M	C	Corrected
1		Leader		20	20	20					
2		Chart		24	25	25					
3		Leader		20	20	20					
4		MLS Man+Woman	Nigh	26	28	20					
5		MS. Man by Window	Int:	26	28	20					
6		MLS Man+Woman	Fire	26	28	20					
7		CU Man	Light	27	29	21					
8		MLS Man+Woman		26	28	20					
9		CU Man		27	29	21					

GRADING FOR THE ANSWER PRINT (1)   (1) An electronic analyser may
be used with a complete cutting copy as scene by scene reference.
(2) Timing data from rush print records or from the analyser is entered on
the appropriate record sheet for each scene.

155

Grading for the Answer Print (2)

Having arrived at the first .estimate of scene-by-scene printer point values for a cut reel by the methods just described, it is next necessary to assess their results. To reduce the cost of wasted labour and film stocks, various methods are adopted to show the grader the results of his first estimates without making a full-length positive print.

Electronic analysers
On some electronic analysers the original negative may be wound through in step with the punched control tape, which alters the red, green and blue channel gain settings for each scene, thus showing the effect of the scene to scene grading. Equipment has also been produced which makes use of a telecine unit, similarly controlled by a punched tape, through which the negative is run at correct action speed to give a colour monitor display as a positive image. Such electronic methods are rapid and allow further corrections to be assessed without any expense of film stock or processing, but they suffer from the difficulty that the character of the picture on the TV monitor differs from that of a projected photographic print. This sometimes makes judgement inexact, especially in very low-key and night-effect scenes.

Photographic tests
An alternative method is to print a very short test section of each scene using the estimated light point values and examine the results on a slide projector. Some specialised optical printers can be programmed to print, for example, a length of 4 frames at the head end of each cut; this allows all the scenes of a complete double reel to be examined at a cost of 50 or 60 feet of stock instead of 2000 feet. A recent development is the Proofing Printer in which a series of single frames can be printed from any selected positions within the cut reel. By the use of such equipment a whole feature length film may be tested with the use of only a hundred feet or so and although the results are stills, they accurately represent the photographic quality of a full-length print.

Another procedure, much used by some laboratories in Europe, is the clipping roll or 'Chenille'. For this a two-frame clip is taken from the tail end trim of each cut as the negative is assembled. These are identified with a scribed scene and take number and spliced together in continuity order. The resultant roll is printed on a regular continuous contact printer at a single light point setting and the corrections necessary estimated visually when the result is viewed frame by frame on a slide projector. However, the selection, identification and joining of the clippings involves a considerable amount of additional labour, and in some cases frames fully representative of the actual scene may not in fact be available in the unused portion of the take.

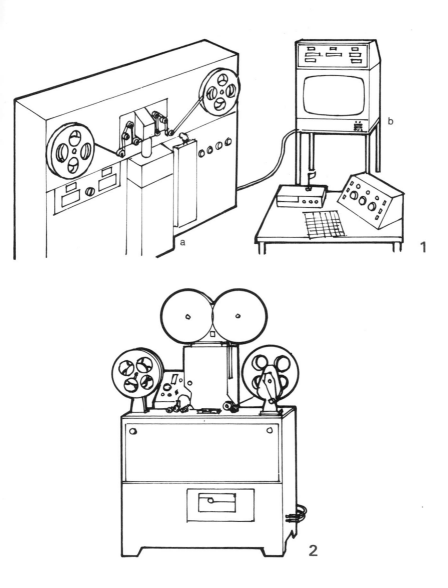

GRADING FOR THE ANSWER PRINT (2)   (1) A negative tele-cine (a) may
be used to check the first timing values on a TV monitor screen (b).
(2) The Proofing Printer allows one frame from each scene in a cut reel to
be printed to verify the first estimated timing values.

Answer Print Stages

All the preceding steps are aimed at ensuring that the first full length print made from the cut picture and track negative is as nearly as possible what the customer requires. This is the first trial composite print. From this point onwards, print assessment and correction is based on the personal judgement of the grader by visual inspection.

The grader will view the first full print in comparison with the cutting copy by running them on two screens side by side in synchronisation and will compare the results he has obtained with those which were initially suggested. In many cases the first print will be fairly close to what is wanted but may show some small inconsistencies of colour balance from scene to scene. A skilled grader will usually be able to estimate the size of the changes required in terms of printer point values from viewing the print at normal projection speed, but in some cases, especially if there are a large number of very short cuts, he may wish to study it further on a slide projector. At this stage colour filters may be temporarily inserted in the projection beam to help in gauging accurately any further correction. Some graders use a wide range of calibrated filters in conjunction with a double-headed still projector, which can show single frames from adjacent scenes against a frame from a guide print or cutting copy. The ability to view a print of two successive scenes at the same time greatly assists in obtaining a uniformly graded result, each preceding scene in turn being regarded as a temporary reference for matching purposes.

Liaison with the production team

In feature film work, even if the grader considers the first print reasonably good, he may wish to have his ideas of further corrections confirmed by the director or cameraman concerned; this is particularly important with colour effects lighting, night sequences and other dramatic styles where there can be considerable variation in the personal judgement of what is correct. If the original rush prints were only in black and white, or required large corrections, the practice of running a first print 'for comments' from the production team often saves trouble later.

Similarly, it is a good precaution to run a print at this early stage with the editor to check any points of sound or picture continuity, especially if this is the first time that optical effects such as fades and dissolves have been seen in their exact context in the reel.

As a result of these first viewings and comments the grader will prepare a scene-by-scene list of printing corrections, and a revised printer control strip will be prepared making these corrections to the original printer point values. A second trial composite print can now be made. At this stage the grader is concerned not only with uniformity from scene to scene but also from one reel to the next.

158

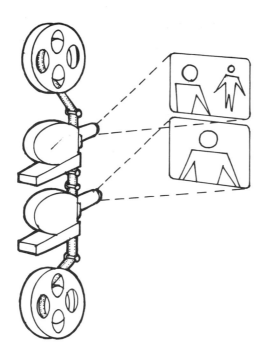

1

L G P	Y	C	M	CORRECTION	L G P	Y	C	M	CORRECTION	L G P	Y	C	M	CORRECTION
1				—	35					69				
2				Curve	36					70				
3				—	37					71				
4	+2	+1	+2	+1D 1R	38					72				
5	0	0	0	OK	39					73				
6	+2	+1	+2	+1D 1R	40					74				
7	+2	0	+2	+2R	41					75				

TIMING RECORD   DATE 12.i.74

SUBJECT A NEW LOOK   VERSION DOM
REEL N? 2   TIMINGS N? 2   RUN N? 41374
N?   GRADER 369   CORR. BY 116

2

ANSWER PRINT STAGES   (1) A double-headed still projector which allows single frames of successive scenes to be compared is useful in correcting a first print. (2) The grader's corrections for viewing are entered on a record sheet and used to prepare a new printer control strip. Note that the corrections are first recorded as the overall effect, "+1 Density +1 Red," and then converted to individual YCM corrections.

Answer Print Presentation

The grader may have to repeat the operations of viewing and correction a number of times before he is satisfied that he has obtained a uniform result in which all the dramatic effects required are correctly balanced. This is then the 'final trial composite print' or 'answer print', which is to be submitted to the production company's representatives for approval, and this approval must precede all general release print production.

Viewing conditions—35mm

Both laboratory and studio must ensure that their viewing conditions are similar, and their screen brightness levels are correctly maintained. In Great Britain the open gate screen luminance standard for 35mm preview theatres is specified as 11 ± 1 foot-lamberts while in the United States the standard is 16 ± 2 foot-lamberts. Unfortunately a difference of 4 ft.L is quite significant and although the viewer's eye does accommodate itself to some extent, a print which is judged satisfactory on a screen of 14 ft.L may appear rather dark at a projection level of 10 ft.L. The situation is even more difficult if an answer print is to be judged in a regular cinema theatre, for example at a sneak preview. For the general run of 35mm motion picture theatres the British Standard permits a range from 8 to 16 ft.L, and the American from 14 to 18; in practice these limits may not be strictly observed. The use of directional screens may add to the problems, particularly with steep projection angles since the apparent brightness seen from the balcony may be very different from that seen from the stalls.

Viewing conditions—16mm

For 16mm answer prints, the review theatre standards are 10 ± 1 ft.L in the United Kingdom and 16 ± 2 ft.L in the United States. But there may also be variations in the type of light source used for projection. 16mm projection has used incandescent tungsten filament lamps with colour temperature of about 3200 K almost exclusively for many years, but Xenon lamps are now becoming quite common. The colour difference between these two light sources is marked, and a print balanced for tungsten projection may look decidedly blue with Xenon; similarly a print corrected for Xenon will appear yellow-orange with tungsten projection.

It is possible to compromise some degree, but it is advisable to instruct the laboratory of the projection light source which will be used for viewing the answer print. It is, however, internationally agreed that 16mm prints intended for telecine should be balanced for projection with a Xenon light source of 5400 K.

160

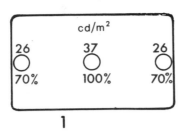

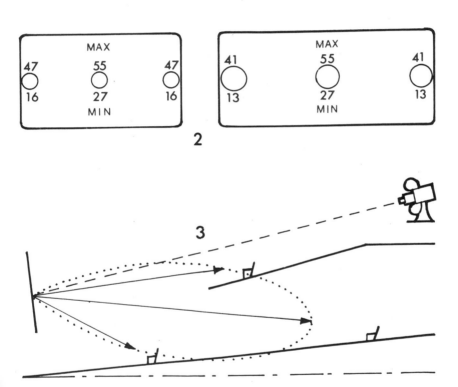

SCREEN BRIGHTNESS VARIATIONS   Laboratory review rooms are normally held closely to the published B.S.I. luminance standard (1) but in cinema theatres wide variations may be found (2), even within the limits allowed. In theatres using directionally reflective screens (3), substantial variations in apparent luminance may be found in different parts of the auditorium, even though the screen is tilted to give the most effective average distribution.

Trailers & Post-Production Work

At one time announcement trailers and other short publicity films for feature productions were assembled from the unused takes left over after editing, but now the required material is almost invariably chosen from the scenes selected for cutting. Often, the final choice is not made until the negative has been assembled in its final reel form.

The creation of such publicity shorts, complete with their super-imposed titles and complex optical effects, is generally carried out by a specialist organisation, but the laboratory cutting the original negative is usually called on to supply intermediates from which the dupe trailer can be prepared. The chosen sections of the cut reel specified by the trailer production company must be printed as 'special scenes' selected from the full length negative, often representing only a few feet out of a total of 1800 feet.

Preparing material for trailers
While it is quite possible to print such sections on a continuous contact printer, threading and un-threading over a series of sprockets in a dark room involves some hazard to the negative. It is preferable to do this sort of work on a step printer with the print stock in a magazine, so that the handling of the picture negative in the middle of a scene can be carried out in the light. An even better procedure is to print the selected sections on an optical step printer, programming the camera head to run only for the required length at the point chosen. In this way, the original negative can be always threaded up in the leader or other spacing sections.

Other post-production work
With the approval of the Answer Print the main part of the laboratory's 'front end' work is complete but there may be a number of post-production details to attend to. These include the selection of material for the preparation of foreign language versions, particularly back-grounds for main and end titles ('textless title BG') and other inserts. Similar background material will be required for foreign language trailers and publicity shorts.

The final tidying-up must include the removal from the laboratory's storage of all material not required for subsequent release print work. Unprinted takes and second negative not used in any way in the final cutting will be condensed by winding on cores into large rolls and re-turned with appropriate identification lists; instructions can be given for any scenes suitable for library use to be spooled separately. Trims from takes used in cutting will also be condensed and identified. Cutting copies, track rush prints, unwanted intermediates, etc., should also be withdrawn as soon as possible after answer print completion.

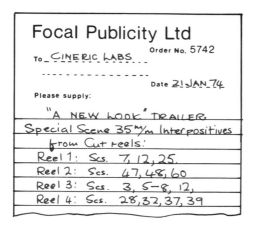

Focal Publicity Ltd

Order No. 5742

To CINERIC LABS

Date 21 JAN 74

Please supply:

"A NEW LOOK" TRAILER.
Special Scene 35 m/m Interpositives
from Cut reels:
Reel 1: Scs. 7, 12, 25.
Reel 2: Scs. 47, 48, 60
Reel 3: Scs. 3, 5—8, 12,
Reel 4: Scs. 28, 32, 37, 39

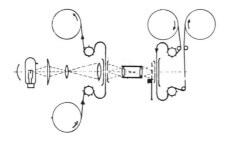

2

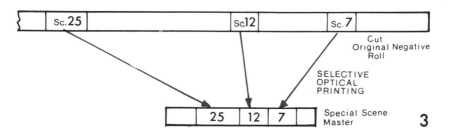

Sc.25   Sc12   Sc.7

Cut
Original Negative
Roll

SELECTIVE
OPTICAL
PRINTING

25   12   7   Special Scene
Master

3

SPECIAL SCENES FOR PUBLICITY TRAILERS To prepare publicity
trailers short sections may be ordered from the cut feature reels (1). To reduce
the handling of the original negative these "special scene" masters can be
printed on an optical printer (2) whose camera head is operated to the
required cue sheet to print only the sections specified (3).

Changes of Format

So far all the laboratory operations described have assumed that the film gauge and frame size of both original negative and resultant print is identical. There are however a number of cases in which this is not the case and the laboratory has to make changes of format by optical printing at one stage or another. The reason for these alterations is usually to provide prints to suit different types of projection equipment in various distribution situations.

Reduction and enlargement

Reduction printing to produce 16mm and 8mm copies from 35mm originals is widely used and now that large area 65mm photography is obsolescent in Western Europe and the United States, 35mm film is the usual source of 70mm copies printed by enlargement. Enlargement printing ('blow-up') is sometimes used to make 35mm copies from a regular 16mm original, but for reasons of quality the use of Super-16 originals is preferred.

Alterations of frame format

A well-known example of this is the preparation of so-called 'Unsqueezed' prints, suitable for normal projection in cinema and television, from an anamorphic original of the Cinemascope type, prints of which require special anamorphic projection lenses. Unsqueezing may also be combined with reduction printing, when making 16mm or 8mm copies from a Cinemascope production. Even apart from anamorphic images, alteration in frame size and composition may be called for when prints with the television aspect ratio of 1·33:1 are required from a wide-screen original of A.R. 1·85:1.

Printers

Although high speed continuous optical printers are available for making 8mm copies, most machines available for enlargement or reduction work are of the intermittent step-printer type and run comparatively slowly. Prints made on such machines are therefore expensive and direct blow-up or reduction from the original is only used where the number of copies required is small. Where large numbers of release prints are needed it usually is much more economical to make an intermediate facility by optical printing once only for the change of format and to run off all further copies by normal contact printing from this.

It should always be recognised that optical printing emphasises the appearance of all dirt, abrasions and other physical defects on the surface of the original; wet printing or liquid gates are therefore essential in all types of format change, whether by reduction or enlargement. Dirt printed into the derived dupe or internegative is perhaps the most serious danger to quality in all operations of this kind.

164

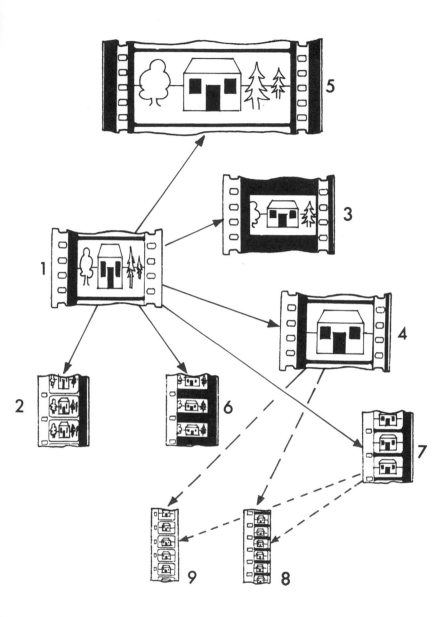

CHANGES OF FORMAT   A 35mm anamorphic picture (1) can be reduced to anamorphic 16mm (2), unsqueezed to 35mm wide-screen (3), 35mm TV format (4), enlarged to 70mm (5) and reduced and unsqueezed to 16mm wide-screen (6) or 16mm TV (7). The unsqueezed frame may be further reduced to Regular 8mm (8) and Super-8 (9).

Enlargement Printing: 16mm to 35mm

Because of convenience and economy 16mm production is often undertaken on subjects intended for general cinema distribution as 35mm copies. Rush printing during photography is straight-forward, but it is the usual practice to make a 35mm blow-up intermediate as soon as the original has been cut so that sound dubbing and final mixing can be done against a 35mm work print from this intermediate. If editing has been satisfactorily completed in the 16mm form, the original will be cut checker-board as A and B rolls so that the resultant intermediate is to its final continuity, including fades and dissolves. On the other hand, if further editing work is likely, the original can be cut overlength and the intermediate made in this form. Final editing is then carried out on a 35mm one-light print from the intermediate, which is subsequently cut to match the revised work print.

The type of intermediate prepared depends on the original 16mm material used: a colour internegative from reversal originals and a colour reversal intermediate (CRI) from original 16mm colour negative. If both types of 16mm original are used in the same production, they must be assembled in separate rolls for blowing-up and the 35mm facility cut to final continuity.

Super-16

The regular 16mm frame size is not well suited for enlargement to the wide-screen 35mm format. For a wide-screen aspect ratio of 1·65:1 or more Super-16 (which has the frame width extended) makes available some 40% greater negative area, so that the enlargement factor is less and the definition improved and grain reduced in the 35mm print.

To handle Super-16, modified cameras with enlarged gate apertures and re-centred lenses must be used with single-perforated 16mm stock only. The laboratory must be equipped to make both full-width 16mm contact prints for rushes and 35mm blow-ups from this larger area.

Super-16 uses normal single-perforated stock for photography but there have been suggestions for a still further increase in frame size by the use of 16mm width stock with the smaller Super-8 type of hole. Such systems have not yet been standardised and since they require specific printing equipment, photography on such material should not be undertaken without the laboratory's confirmation that it can be handled.

Remember that the Super-16 system is designed solely for enlargement to widescreen 35mm: there is no Super-16 format for 16mm contact-printed release copies. Neither is there any advantage in using Super-16 photography for subjects to be shown in the 1·33:1 aspect ratio, as on television, either 35 or 16mm.

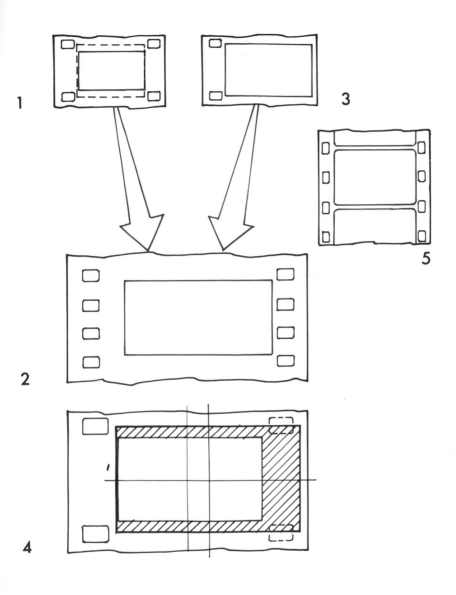

16MM BLOW-UP   Only part of the standard 16mm frame area (1) is
used for enlargement to 35mm wide screen (2). The Super-16 frame (3) allows
greater area to be used, approximately 40% more (4). Another proposed
form of Super-16 uses 16mm stock perforated with the smaller perforation
holes used in Super-8 (5).

Enlargement Printing: 35mm to 70mm

70mm projection still provides the highest quality of motion picture presentation available in the entertainment theatre, but the expense of photography is so high that production in this format has virtually ceased in Western Europe and the United States, although 70mm negative continues in use in the USSR. Elsewhere 70mm prints are now made by enlargement printing from a 35mm original and since the number of copies required is small, they are usually made directly on an optical printer and not by way of an intermediate.

Anamorphic negatives

The best results are obtained from a 35mm anamorphic negative of the Cinemascope type, composed for an aspect ratio of 2·35:1 for normal 35mm release. The 70mm print is obtained by anamorphic enlargement, so that the horizontal magnification of the optical system is twice that in the vertical direction, and the resultant image is projected to an aspect ratio of 2·2:1. This is sufficiently close to the original A.R. of 2·35:1 to be acceptable for all normal composition but care should be taken with titles to see that wording does not come so close to the edge of the 35mm frame that it might be cut off in 70mm.

If it is known in advance that a 35mm subject is to be shown as 70mm copies, the original negative can be cut as A and B rolls and fades and dissolves included during the enlargement printing. Checkerboard cutting is not however necessary, since narrow 35mm negative splices will not show in the projected area of the 70mm print.

Flat negatives

70mm copies can also be made from regular (non-anamorphic) wide-screen 35mm originals, but the enlargement factor is considerable and both grain and loss of image sharpness may be objectionable. In addition, to obtain a 2·2:1 aspect ratio frame from an original composition of 1·65:1 means the loss of picture area from top and bottom of the picture and may result in unacceptable cropping of head-lines. From an original composition of 1·85:1 this cropping is less marked but may still be serious wherever the original action was tight at the top of the frame.

16mm originals

Even 16mm originals have been blown-up to 70mm, but the magnification is so great and the loss of image quality so marked that the results are only acceptable in very special cases.

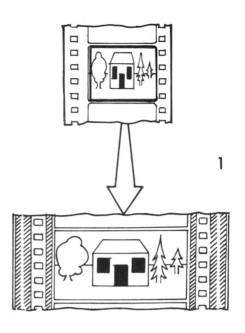

1

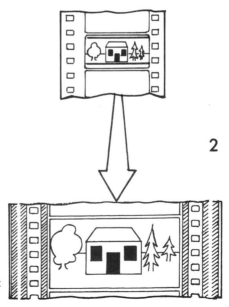

2

BLOW-UP TO 70MM
(1) 70mm prints are often made by anamorphic (unsqueezing) enlargement from a 35mm Cinemascope type original.
(2) They can be made by straight blow-up from 35mm wide-screen but the original area used is very small.

Unsqueeze Printing

Prints suitable for normal 'flat' projection without special lenses or for use on telecine machines for television transmissions may have to be made from anamorphic original negatives. Such de-anamorphosed or 'unsqueezed' prints can be made on an optical printer with a suitable anamorphic copy lens system.

It is important to recognise that all flat prints have a less wide aspect ratio than that of the projected anamorphic original, 2·35:1, so that some loss of composition at the sides of the picture is inevitable. For 35mm, unsqueezed prints can be made with any aspect ratio from 1·65:1 to 1·85:1, the latter ratio being frequently used since it represents the least sacrifice of picture width (over 10% from each side). However, the alteration of composition is often noticeable, especially with titles. In 16mm, unsqueezed prints for normal projection are generally made to A.R. 1·65:1, so as to yield the largest print area, but losing nearly 15% from each side. It is normal practice to retain the full height of the original composition in making unsqueezed prints in any other aspect ratio.

Prints for television from anamorphic negatives

The proportions of the normal television screen are approximately 4 by 3 (A.R. 1·33). An unsqueezed print of this A.R. loses almost half the width of the composition in the anamorphic original, and important action within the picture is likely to be lost if the area printed is always selected from the middle of the frame. The print is therefore made so that the most important area of action is chosen from the full width of composition. If necessary the area selected is varied during the shot to keep the centre of interest within the printed area. This is termed 'pan and scan' printing and must be done on an optical printer whose unsqueezing lens can be moved during running to copy the part of the negative selected. In general, five or seven positions can be selected within the frame area and the lens can be moved between frames from one to another or it can be panned between them over a pre-determined number of frames. The whole programme of selected areas for a complete reel must be worked out in advance, and a control tape prepared to move the printer lens as required. Pan and scan printing is thus an expensive operation and where only one transmission print is required there is an increasing trend to use a regular anamorphic copy and perform the pan and scan selection electronically at the telecine stage. When a large number of transmission prints are required, as in general 16mm use, a pan and scan reduction dupe negative (usually CRI), from which contact prints can be made, may be prepared.

170

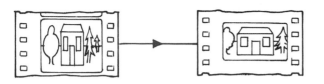

1

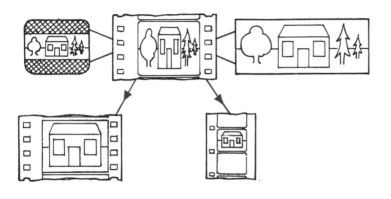

2

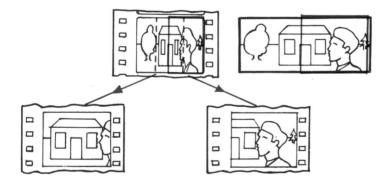

3

UNSQUEEZE PRINTING   (1) 35mm wide-screen copies of A.R. 1.65:1 to 1.85:1 can be made from 35mm anamorphic original negative.
(2) Unsqueezing to 35mm or 16mm prints of the TV aspect ratio of 1.33:1 loses a considerable part of the original composition.
(3) To avoid important action being lost the area of the original should be selected to follow the action on a pan-and-scan printer.

Reduction Printing: 35mm to 16mm

The preparation of 16mm copies from a 35mm original negative is a very frequent laboratory requirement, since 16mm prints are widely used for special distribution situations such as mobile cinemas, on aircraft and ships and in a range of commercial and educational requirements.

Where the original 35mm photography has been composed to the original Academy standard format of aspect ratio approximately 1·37:1, the preparation of 16mm prints or duplicate negatives presents no problems, since the projected aspect ratio of the 16mm copy is almost identical, at 1·33:1.

However, in the majority of cases the 35mm original has been composed for widescreen presentation, say of aspect ratio 1·65:1, and the laboratory must be advised of the format required in the resultant 16mm print. If the original composition is to be retained in full the height of the picture image will not fill the height of the 16mm frame and prints must be made with a wide black inter-frame area. If a reduction-printed colour reversal intermediate is being prepared it must be double-printed with a suitable inter-frame matte to give this effect. On the other hand, if the full height of the 16mm frame is to be occupied by the full height of the original composition, it must be realised that there will be some loss of picture at the sides of the 16mm print, corresponding to some 10% on each edge lost from a 1·65:1 original and over 15% from 1·85:1. The decision as to the format required should not be left to the laboratory, since complaints of unwanted cut-off are only too likely.

Printing methods

Individual 16mm copies may be made by direct optical reduction printing on to the positive stock, but where quantities of prints are wanted it is always more economical to make a reduction intermediate from which the cheaper contact prints can be taken. 16mm reduction intermediates can be supplied in several forms and the laboratory's choice will be determined by the number of copies required and their particular processing equipment. A single 16mm intermediate suitable for printing on a standard 16mm contact printer is the simplest form, but for long production runs dual-rank 16mm intermediates on either 32mm or 35mm width stock allow rapid and economical operation. The twin-16 on 32 type can be made in two forms, on stock perforated with holes in the 1—4 position, with the two 16mm prints running in opposite directions, and on 1—3 perforated stock, where both run in the same direction. The latter has the advantage that the two picture images on the intermediate can be printed simultaneously by the use of a beam-splitting prism on the optical reduction printer.

A corresponding 16mm sound track will have to be re-recorded from the magnetic master in all cases.

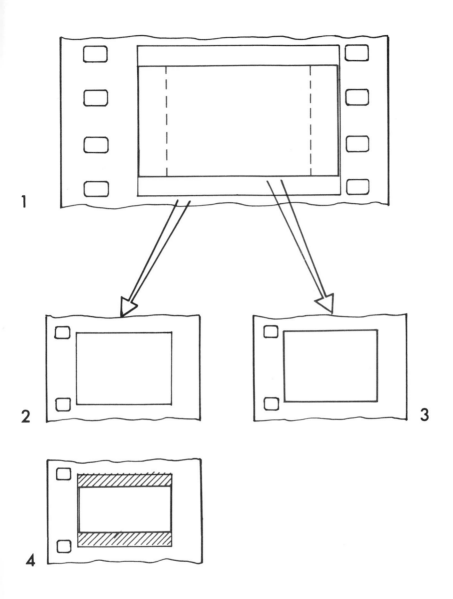

REDUCTION PRINTING TO 16MM   Reduction from the original Academy
frame (1) satisfactorily fills the standard 16mm frame (2) but from 35mm
wide-screen, reduction to 16mm must either lose composition at the sides (3)
or use less than the full height of the 16mm frame (4).

Reduction Printing to 8mm & Super-8

8mm copies are almost always made by reduction from larger gauge originals, since production photography and editing in 8mm is not yet considered satisfactory for professional use. Since 8mm distribution often calls for large numbers of prints, these are generally produced by way of reduction intermediates and contact printing, although continuous optical reduction printers are now available which can print 8mm copies very rapidly from a 16mm original or intermediate. Like television, the format of the 8mm frame, both regular and Super-8, has the 4 × 3 proportions, so that both 35 and 16mm originals intended for reduction to 8mm must have an aspect ratio of 1·33:1.

Multi-rank intermediates

8mm intermediates can be made in several forms, either as two rows on 16mm width film or as four rows on 35mm. The 16mm width stock may be perforated with two rows of holes in the 1–4 position (both outer edges), in which case the two 8mm copies run head-to-tail in opposite directions, or in the 1–3 position (edge and centre), when the two prints run in the same direction. The arrangement of four 8mm prints on a 35 width strip is normally with all running in the same direction.

Multi-rank intermediates in these forms can be made for both the regular 8mm gauge (8mm Type R) and for Super-8 (8mm Type S) but it must be remembered that these are not interchangeable: if both types of print are required, two separate sets of intermediates will have to be prepared.

In general, 8mm prints with sound are only made for normal release in the Super-8 form and both photographic and magnetic sound tracks are in use. When ordering a re-recorded sound negative for 8mm release prints it is therefore essential to specify the gauge and type of multi-row picture intermediate with which it will be used as well as the A or B roll winding. Magnetic sound is usually transferred directly to the print from a 16mm magnetic master.

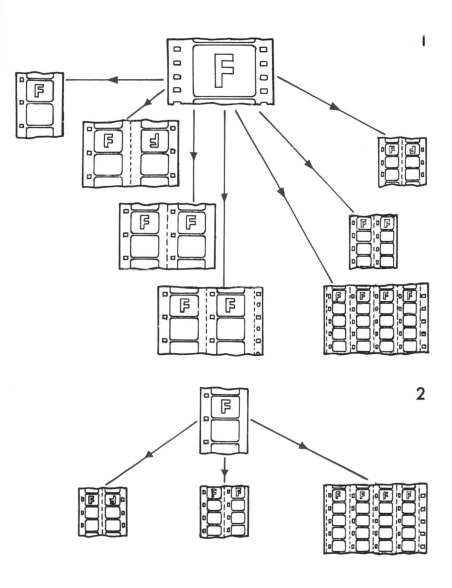

REDUCTION PRINTING TO 16MM AND 8MM (1) 35mm originals may be reduced to 16 and 8mm in several forms, with both double and quadruple rows of images. (2) Similarly, 16mm reduction to 8mm can be in both two and four row systems.

Magnetic Sound

The requirements for prints with magnetic sound should be clearly understood so that appropriate instructions can be given for processing when copies are to be delivered from the laboratory for subsequent striping and recording as separate operations. Such prints must be of correct length to match the magnetic master and must not have been shortened by the removal of one or two frames at a raw stock join. Some laboratories automatically wax or lubricate the edges of all prints manufactured but this may make subsequent magnetic striping difficult and the wax may have to be cleaned off before a stripe can be applied. Instructions to the laboratory should therefore clearly indicate 'full length unwaxed print for magnetic striping.'

Specification of magnetic stripes

The position and widths of magnetic sound stripes on prints are now internationally standardised; 70mm prints always take magnetic sound with six tracks for stereophonic presentation on four stripes. Although at one time stereosound was an important part of Cinemascope presentation with 35mm prints, it is now somewhat infrequent and where used, copies are made with both photographic and magnetic tracks, as combined MAG-OPT prints capable of being used on normal projectors as well as those fitted with magnetic heads. Four magnetic stripes are coated on 35mm film having the smaller perforation hole, Type CS.

Although only one magnetic stripe is used to carry the sound on 16mm and 8mm prints, it is normal practice to apply a second narrower stripe along the opposite edge of the film in the margin outside the perforations. This is termed the balance stripe and compensates for the extra thickness of the film where the sound stripe is applied, which might otherwise make winding and spooling somewhat irregular.

Sound synchronization

Uniform international standards exist for the synchronisation of picture and magnetic sound for 70, 35 and 16mm copies, but in both regular 8mm and Super-8 different projectors have different specifications. Although many Super-8 machines have adopted a uniform magnetic sound advance of 18 frames, which is the British Standard, others show variations from an advance of 125 frames for Bohn Benton down to a 40 frame retard on the Jayarc projector.

For regular 8mm the British Standard gives no uniform practice and projectors with sound head positions varying from 60 frame advance to 28 frame retard may be found. When ordering magnetic sound on 8mm copies, both regular and Super-8, it is therefore essential to specify the synchronisation required or the type of projector on which the prints will be used.

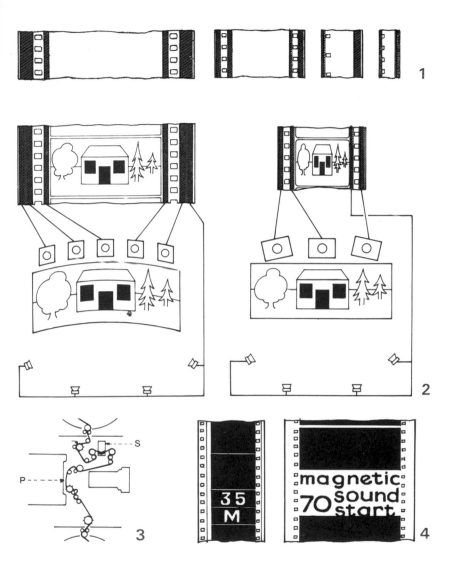

MAGNETIC SOUND (1) Magnetic sound tracks are used on 70mm, 35mm, 16mm and Super-8 prints. (2) Multiple tracks allow stereophonic presentation from both 70mm and 35mm copies. (3) In the projector the position of the magnetic sound head S above the picture gate P means that magnetic tracks are printed behind the corresponding picture for correct synchronisation.
(4) Thread-up frame on 35mm and 70mm leaders show the correct position in the sound head relative to the picture START frame.

177

Release Printing from 35mm Negative

We will now consider the various methods of making release prints for general distribution once the original negative has been cut and the answer print approved. At this stage, the bulk production aspects of laboratory operations are an important factor, so that economic high-speed printing methods must be considered in conjunction with print quality and the safety of the original material.

Where the original is a 35mm colour negative there are three possible routes for making contact printed 35mm release copies of the picture:

(a)   direct from the original negative;

(b)   by way of a colour duplicate printed from a colour master;

(c)   by way of a colour reversal intermediate negative (CRI) optically printed from the original.

Direct printing from the original negative undoubtedly gives optimum print quality and will always be used in making the first run copies for special presentations. On the other hand, repeated use of the original for making large numbers of release prints may be considered too hazardous.

The use of a duplicate negative from a master positive was the most general procedure for release printing for many years, but it had to be recognised that some loss of colour quality and general visibility was usual. With the introduction of reversal intermediate stock the use of CRI's has become the preferred method of release printing which best maintains the quality of the original. Reversal intermediates printed with the scene-to-scene grading corrections applicable to the original negative should be completely uniform and can be printed throughout at a single light level. Such 'one-light' facilities can therefore be used to make release prints at the highest speed of which the printing machine is capable.

Making 16mm prints

16mm prints may also be made from the 35mm negative by similar routes, either by direct optical reduction or by contact printing from a reduction CRI. Direct reduction yields good quality copies, but is slow and involves repeated use of the original negative, so that the use of a reduction CRI is the preferred method. 16mm colour dupe negatives were at one time made by reduction from a 35mm colour master positive but the CRI route now gives superior quality. When black and white release prints are required from a colour negative it is again possible to produce them in two ways either by direct printing from the original on to a panchromatic black and white positive stock, or by way of a dupe negative made from a black and white panchromatic master. Since the latter method allows release printing on the less expensive regular black and white positive material, it is to be preferred if a large number of copies are needed.

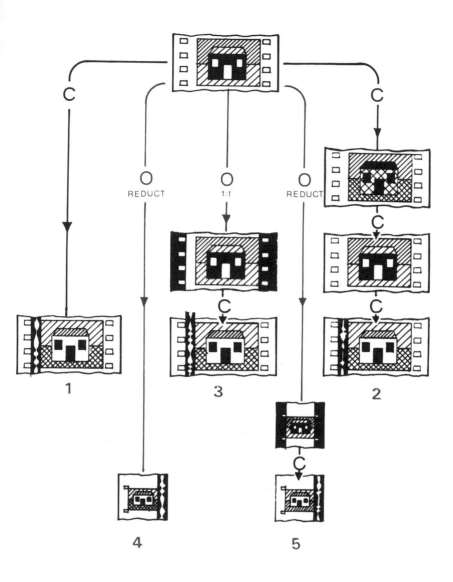

RELEASE PRINTING FROM 35MM NEGATIVES 35mm copies can be made by contact direct from the original negative (1), by way of a contact printed dupe negative (2), or from an optically printed reversal intermediate (3). 16mm reduction prints are made either by direct optical printing (4) or from a reduction reversal intermediate (5).

179

Release Printing from 16mm Reversal

16mm copies from 16mm reversal originals may be produced in three ways as contact prints:

(a) direct from the original on to a suitable reversal print stock;

(b) by way of a duplicate reversal master, again on to reversal print stock;

(c) by way of an internegative on to regular positive stock.

Direct printing gives good quality but involves continued use of the original for all copies; also, as noted earlier, different types of reversal originals may require the use of different print materials, so that intercutting originals may present problems in direct printing.

The use of a duplicate master protects the original and if made to include fade and dissolve effects, can avoid the trouble and expense of A and B roll printing for every release print. However, it still involves the use of the more expensive reversal print stock.

For general release printing the cheapest method is undoubtedly the use of an internegative incorporating all optical effects with regular positive stock, although some lowering of colour quality and definition must be expected in comparison with a direct reversal copy.

Making 35mm prints

Where 35mm release prints are to be made from a 16mm reversal original (or equally from Super-16 reversal) the only recommended procedure is by way of an enlargement internegative from which contact prints can be made on to regular positive stock. The internegative will be printed from the original A and B cut rolls and will incorporate all fades, dissolves and other effects.

Should black and white prints be required the 16 or 35 internegative will be made on a panchromatic duplicating stock and release prints made on regular black and white positive.

180

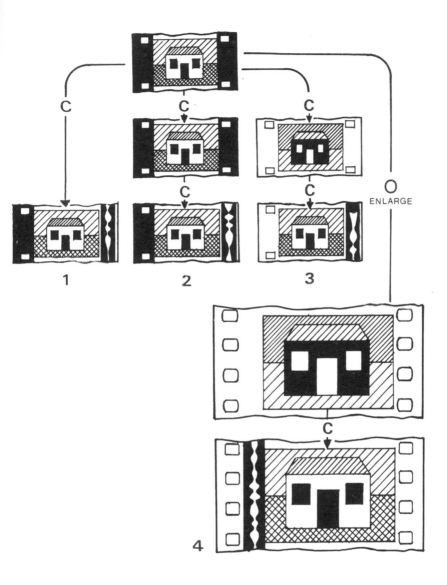

RELEASE PRINTING FROM 16MM REVERSAL 16mm contact prints
can be made as reversal copies from the original (1), or by way of a duplicate
reversal master (2), or as positive prints from a contact internegative (3).
35mm copies will normally be made as positive prints by contact from an
optically enlarged internegative (4).

Release Printing from 16mm Negative

16mm prints

The options for release printing from 16mm colour negatives are:
(a) direct from the original negative;
     or
(b) by way of a colour reversal intermediate.

While retaining the best quality, the former hazards the negative through repeated use and involves every copy being double-printed from A and B rolls to obtain fades and dissolves. The use of a CRI on the other hand protects the original, avoids A and B printing and allows high printing speeds from a one-light facility.

It should be noted that in making the 16mm CRI it may be printed either optically or by contact from the original; this is permissible because 16mm copies for projection either 'emulsion to lens' or 'emulsion to lamp' are both acceptable. Care must be taken however to ensure that the correct type of photographic sound track, 'A' winding or 'B' winding, is supplied to correspond.

35mm prints

For 35mm prints from a 16mm or Super-16 negative the use of an enlargement CRI must be regarded as the only acceptable method and from this regular colour positive copies may be contact printed in the usual way.

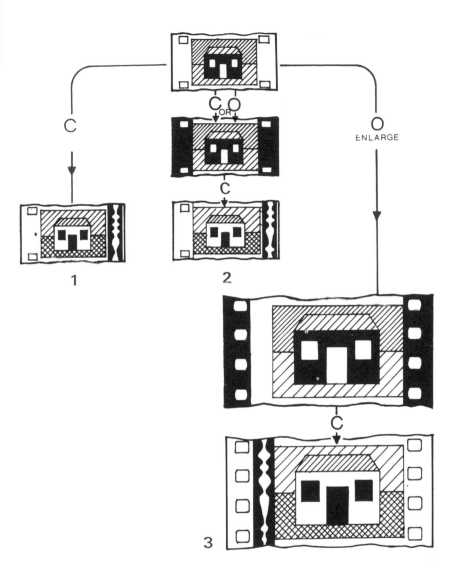

RELEASE PRINTING FROM 16MM NEGATIVE 16mm positive copies are printed either direct from the original negative (1) or from a reversal intermediate (2), which can be either contact or optically printed depending on the print geometry required. 35mm copies are always made from an enlargement reversal intermediate (3).

Release Print Methods

The printing and developing equipment used for release print production is generally very similar to that used at earlier stages but with the emphasis on high speed operation with minimum film handling. For example, picture and track images are always printed at one passage of the positive stock. Panel printers are particularly well suited for release printing from long reels, since once the picture and track negative have been threaded up they can be run forwards and back to make repeated copies with only replacement of the positive stock rolls. At this stage positive stock is used in as large rolls as possible, up to 3000 feet in length, to simplify handling.

Splices in release prints

The sequential use of rolls of positive raw stock on repetition release prints means of course that splices between stock rolls may occur within the picture sequence. It is generally accepted by the laboratories that not more than one raw stock splice should appear in the length of a 1000 foot 35mm release print or in 400 foot 16mm. It is usual practice to supply answer prints and TV commercials without any stock joins in their length but other copies specially ordered as 'spliceless' will be charged at a higher print price.

The aim of the technical control section of a laboratory is to maintain the overall process of printing and developing in a steady condition so that standard prints of uniform quality can be produced with the minimum spoilage rate. Batches of raw stock are carefully checked for photographic speed and colour balance before bringing them into use and regular sensitometric tests on printers and developing machines are supplemented with routine chemical analysis and correction of all processing solutions to ensure uniformity. Many laboratories insert a few frames of a standard reference negative in the head leader of all full length reels and a visual inspection of the print of this appearing in all release copies provides a rapid confirmation that the overall process is running satisfactorily. Track densities on release prints are also checked by measurements taken at a marked point near the head or tail ends to ensure consistent results.

In addition, release prints are inspected by projection viewing to check that their general colour and density are acceptable and that they are free from serious defects such as dirt, abrasion and scratches. The inspection viewer has a reference print or clipping of each production subject against which he can compare the release print in case of doubt.

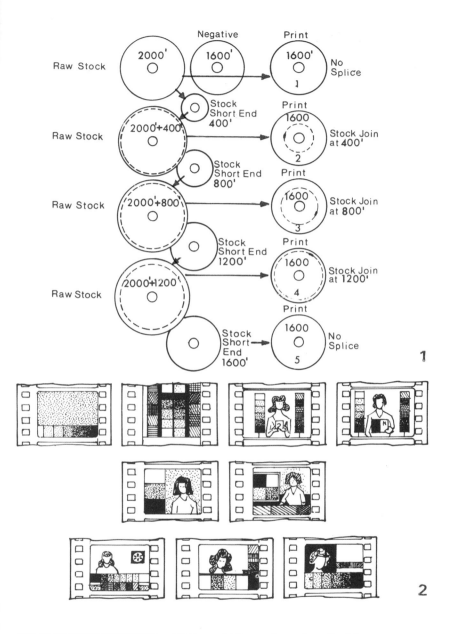

RELEASE PRINT METHODS (1) To avoid the wastage of raw stock in printing, the residual "short end" left over after printing a reel on a full length manufacturer's roll will be spliced on to the next raw stock roll. A stock join will therefore appear in the resultant print. (2) Many laboratories use a few frames of standard negative cut into the head or tail leader to give a visual check of process performance. With the importance of television usage, gray scales are now arranged horizontally in the frame so that they can be assessed on the waveform monitor of a tele-cine machine.

Positive Assembly Work

The final viewing and inspection of release prints completes the actual manufacturing process, but further work is necessary before copies are ready for delivery.

When prints have been processed as A and B sections of less than 1000 feet of 35mm, the two portions will normally be joined before despatch. At the same time, any separately processed main and end titles will be added, together with prints of the appropriate censor certificates and distributor's trade marks. Intermission titles may also be required in the middle of a long feature. Any deletions for censorship or other reasons will also be made at this stage.

Similar make-up work will be required on alternative language versions for foreign distribution and for these, not only main credit and end titles will have to be replaced but other insert scenes and narrative titles must be exchanged for the translated equivalent.

After positive assembly work is complete, each part is given a copy number and the individual parts grouped to provide a complete print.

After-treatment of prints

35mm prints are sometimes given lubrication in the perforation area only (edge-waxing) for safe projection; this treatment may be applied in the course of processing as a final step, or as a separate operation. Protective treatment of the emulsion or base surfaces to increase resistance to scratches and abrasions is usually a separate service.

16mm print finishing is generally similar, although lubrication treatment is often applied over the whole width of the film rather than just the perforated edge. Where release prints have been processed as double-rank 16mm it is convenient to apply this treatment at the stage of slitting to 16mm width. 16mm prints of feature films are often assembled before despatch into reels of 1600 feet in length, representing two double reels of 2000 feet in 35mm, while for television use a single assembly of 50 minutes running time (1800 feet) is often convenient.

8mm release print practice is not yet standardised and the use of a variety of different cartridge and cassette-loaded projectors necessitates exact instructions to the laboratory. All systems require good lubrication over both surfaces of the print and some of the endless loop cartridges require very special lubrication treatment for satisfactory running.

8mm prints are practically never supplied on cores because of the hazard of handling a loosely wound roll, but several projection systems take film wound on a spool which can be inserted into a cassette. Where such systems use automatic rewind devices the tail end of the film leader must be firmly attached to the spool centre. When ordering 8mm or Super-8mm prints it is therefore essential to specify the projector, lubrication and cassette system required.

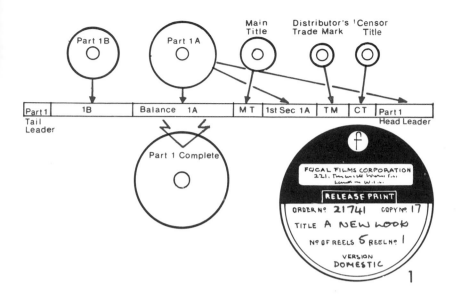

Part 1B Part 1A Main Title Distributor's Trade Mark Censor Title

| Part 1 | 1B | Balance 1A | M T | 1st Sec 1A | T M | C T | Part 1 |

Tail Leader

Head Leader

Part 1 Complete

FOCAL FILMS CORPORATION
221. ‌‌‌‍‌ ‌‌‌‍‌ ‌‌‌‍‌
‌‌‌‍‌ ‌‌‌‍‌

RELEASE PRINT
ORDER No. 21741   COPY No. 17
TITLE A NEW LOOK
No OF REELS 5 REEL No. 1
VERSION
DOMESTIC

1

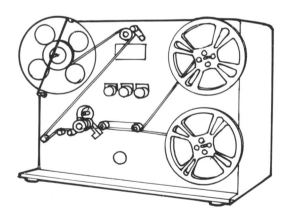

2

POSITIVE ASSEMBLY WORK   (1) Final print assembly may require joining A and B part reels, inserting censor titles and distributor trade marks, checking raw stock joins and deleting any censored sequences.

The last stages in 8mm print handling will involve slitting (2), lubricating and winding on spools or loading into cassettes.

Processing Film for Television

Conditions for viewing film in a darkened cinema theatre are very different from those for television in a lighted living room, and when black and while films were reproduced over the television system it was soon found that prints satisfactory for normal projection appeared too contrasty on television. The tonal range which could be well reproduced was smaller, so that shadow gradation would be lost.

Black and white prints
Lower contrast prints can be made for television, either by shortening the positive developer bath time or by using special low contrast positive stocks. The desirable density range of a television print is from 0·35, representing a white object, to 2·0 or less representing black, with mid-scale face densities falling about 0·80. In a normal projection print, the density range is much greater, from 0·20 or less up to 3·0.

A negative photographed with too high a contrast of lighting and subject matter is unsatisfactory on television even when printed on low contrast stock. Guidelines to limit the contrast at the stage of original photography have therefore been laid down, of which the most important is the recommendation to limit the lighting contrast (ratio of key plus filler to filler alone) to approximately 2:1. Extremes of subject contrast can also be limited by using white materials of not greater than 70% reflectance and blacks of not less than 4%.

Colour prints
Similar considerations apply to colour film for television use. At one time the use of a special low contrast colour positive stock was recommended, particularly in Europe. Such low contrast materials tend to show lower colour saturation and their use was never favoured in the United States, where control of contrast in initial photography is preferred.

With improvement in telecine equipment and greater experience in lighting television film, the use of low contrast colour positive film has decreased considerably. In general it is only used for making prints of old subjects which were not photographed with television limitations in mind.

It is still desirable that colour prints for television use should have minimum densities of 0·3 to 0·4 and shadow areas in which detailed gradation is to be seen should not exceed 2·0, although maximum black may reach 2·5.

Black and white prints from colour negatives may be made by direct printing on to a special panchromatic positive stock developed to low contrast.

1

2

FILM FOR TELEVISION   As compared with projection in a darkened theatre (1), film reproduced on the television screen (2) will apparently show higher contrast, so the tonal range of prints for television use must be kept within stated limits.

189

Viewing Prints for Television Use

Both 35mm and 16mm colour prints intended for television use are required balanced for projection at a colour temperature of 5400 ± 400°K and Xenon lamps are widely used for this purpose in laboratories and review rooms. As noted on the previous page, prints best suited for television will have a lower tonal range and will tend to appear rather flat when seen under regular cinema theatre conditions. It is also recognised that the conditions of television viewing in the home, with ambient room lighting, make inconsistencies and variations of colour reproduction more obvious than in a darkened theatre where the viewer's eye quickly accommodates.

Viewing conditions

The ideal method of print inspection is, of course, an accurately lined-up telecine with closed circuit reproduction on a monitor, but since this is expensive and inconvenient, optical projection conditions to simulate its effect have been developed. These provide for the presentation of a comparatively small picture at a high brightness level with a large uniformly illuminated surround of the same colour as the projector light source. The surround luminance should be between one-third and one-quarter that of a white object in the projected film image; in practice this means a surround level of 8 to 12 candela per square metre for an open gate screen luminance of 100 cd/m².

The surround should extend a distance at least equal to the width of the picture in all directions around the screen and the picture should be viewed from a distance of five to six times its height. Provided the conditions of relative brightness and matched colour are met, picture and surround can be produced by front or rear illumination as convenient.

The effect of the surround is to condition the viewer's eye so that the contrast of the picture is similar to that obtained on television transmission, while this large apparently grey area provides a reference field against which variations of colour grading and reel uniformity can be very critically judged.

It is desirable that any projector used for TV print viewing should be supplied with interchangeable masks cut to represent the transmitted and safe areas of the television film so that questions of title or action cut-off can be quickly decided.

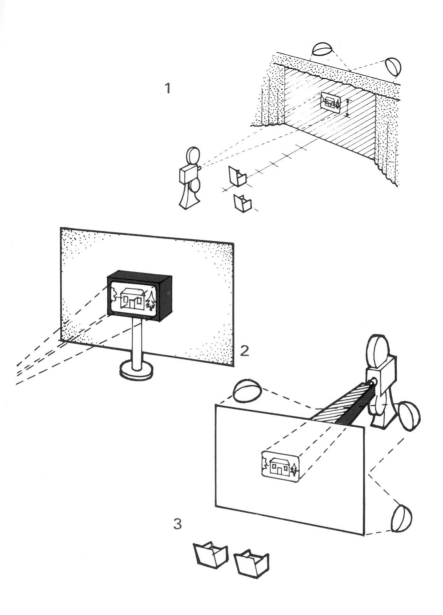

VIEWING PRINTS FOR TELEVISION   To simulate the effect of television, prints for telecine use should be viewed by projection on a small screen within an illuminated surround. This may be a translucent panel lit from behind (1) or a flat wall illuminated by lamps mounted behind the small screen (2). Alternatively back-projection along an enclosed tunnel on to the translucent panel may be used (3).

The Use of Film on Television

Film plays many important parts in television programmes, one of which is of course its use for old feature films. Film material specifically produced for television falls into four categories:

News and real life documentary subjects (usually location)
Readily portable cameras are essential, so 16mm equipment is practically standard and in the United States some local stations are using Super-8. For news work reversal films are general, often processed on small developing machines at the television centre. Reversal stocks are also widely used for documentary programmes, which are subsequently edited as A and B rolls from which a 16mm graded reversal print is made for transmission or video-tape transfer.

Full length drama subjects and series
These may be produced completely on film, in both studio and location work. 35mm negative is recognised as yielding excellent quality, and all major productions in the United States are filmed on such stock. Starting with 35mm originals, 35mm or 16mm colour reversal intermediates can be made for international distribution without serious loss of quality, as well as black and white dupes if necessary. However, many subjects in this group must be shot on 16mm for economy. In Canada, reversal originals in A and B rolls are used while in Great Britain and Japan 16mm colour negative is general to produce a 16mm colour positive print for transmission, often from A and B assembled rolls.

Film inserts forming parts of television studio productions
35mm negative is often used, but there is increasing use of 16mm colour negative. Improved colour quality and reduced grain may be obtained by direct negative transfer to video-tape and the procedure is being introduced both for inserts and for full-length programmes.

Advertising spots and commercials
These are generally produced and distributed as film, although there is increasing use of cassette loaded video-tape machines to fill the commercial break. Photography is almost always on 35mm colour negative and the need to obtain effective visual impact in the space of half a minute or less leads to the wide use of ingenious and often elaborate trick effects. The result thus displays a wide range of opticals and the whole length often consists entirely of dupe negative produced by specialist organisations. Release prints are required in large quantities for distribution to TV stations and are made by printing from the negative joined in an endless loop to reduce thread-up operations.

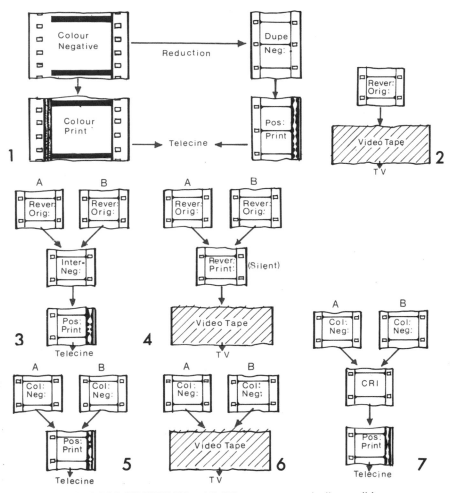

FILM METHODS FOR TELEVISION   (1) Wherever economically possible,
the use of 35mm negative and prints is preferred; 16mm dupes and prints can
be made for wide-spread distribution.

(2) For news work, 16mm reversal is widely used and often edited on to
video-tape for transmission.

(3) 16mm reversal is often used for documentary and educational programmes;
if the subject is to be used for normal projection as well as TV, an internegative
will be made from the A and B original rolls.

(4) However, if it is required for television only, an A and B reversal print may
be made and transferred to video-tape.

(5) In England and Japan 16mm colour negative is used to make an A and B
positive print, but . . .

(6) the negative may also be transferred direct to tape without any positive
print stage.

(7) For international distribution a colour reversal intermediate will be made
from the A and B negatives so that positive prints can be produced in quantity.

193

Laboratory Charges & Budgeting (1)

Because laboratory work is a series of technical operations, often described in unfamiliar jargon, production managers and financial controllers may feel confused at the variety of items which appear on a laboratory's billing advice and suspicious of charges which they have difficulty in relating to matters under their direct control.

General principles

1. Raw stock costs per unit length reflect primarily the manufacturing complexity of the material, secondly its size (gauge) and thirdly whether it is a specialised or a generally used product. Thus, all multi-layer colour materials are more expensive than the simpler black-and-white stocks, but a special product such as colour reversal intermediate is costlier than the widely used colour positive. Length for length, 16mm is cheaper than 35mm film, but not in strict proportion because many of the costs of perforating, film finishing and packing are equal for both sizes.

2. Processing costs similarly reflect the complexity of the operation and the speed with which it can be carried out. Developing 35mm colour negative is more complex and therefore more expensive than black-and-white, but processing 16mm is not necessarily cheaper than 35mm. One-light colour rush prints are cheaper than fully-graded ones because the operation is simpler and the spoilage lower, even though exactly the same film stock and processing is employed.

3. Some work must be charged as a unit, rather than on the basis of length. Negative cutting is a case in point: there may even be more work in cutting a reel of 700 feet with 120 scenes than one of 950 feet with 40 scenes and there is certainly more labour and material involved in checker-board cutting a 400 foot reel of 16mm.

4. Similarly, the work of setting-up printing equipment for special conditions is the same item of expense whether 15 or 500 feet are then printed; optical effects therefore usually take a fixed charge in addition to the charge for the length of film produced.

UNIT COSTS

Prices can differ widely between laboratories and will of course alter from time to time; the following examples from 1973 price lists in England and the United States must only be taken as a general guide.

CONSULT YOUR LABORATORY'S *CURRENT* LIST.

Production Charges	35 mm price per foot			
	B & W Neg/Pos		Colour Neg/Pos	
	Pence	$	Pence	$
Negative Raw Stock	2.4	.06	6.0	.15
Negative Developing	1.1	.03	1.8	.08
„ „ (Forced Dev.)	—	—	2.4	.10
Rush Prints : B & W	2.3	.06	2.3	.07
„ „ : One-light Colour	—	—	4.5	.20
„ „ : Graded Colour	—	—	6.5	.30
Master Positive	3.0	.07	22.5	.45
Dupe Negative	5.0	.11	24.5	.48
Col. Rev. Intermediate	—	—	35.0	.90
3-c Separation Masters (set of 3)	—	—	28.5	.48
Answer Print (1st Trial Composite)	2.5	.08	8.0	.40

	16 mm price per foot			
	Col. Reversal		Colour Neg/Pos	
	Pence	$	Pence	$
Camera Raw Stock	3.1	.07	3.4	.08
Processing Camera Original	2.0	.08	1.8	.08
„ „ (Forced Dev.)	2.5	.11	2.4	.10
Rush Prints : B & W	3.6	.08	2.3	.08
„ „ : One-light Colour	6.7	.15	4.0	.12
„ „ : Graded Colour	8.7	.20	6.0	.20
Colour Master	15.0	.25	14.5	.25
Colour Internegative	18.7	.30	14.5	.25
Col. Rev. Intermediate	—	—	22.5	.45
Answer Print (1st Trial Composite)	8.7	.25	8.5	.20
Charge for A & B Printing	1.5	.05	1.5	.05

Negative Cutting may be charged on the basis of time involved (£3 to £4 or $12 to $15 per hour) or per unit reel of 1000′ 35mm or 400′ 16mm :

Normal Picture	£18 to £19	$75 to $90 per reel
A & B Reels	£26 to £32	$105 to $130 per pair
Checkerboard	£38 to £40	$150 to $180 per pair

plus charge for standard leaders, titles and A & B black spacing.

Laboratory Charges & Budgeting (2)

Outline Budget

An initial production budget must therefore cover a series of items based on the estimated footage used, together with the appropriate unit operations, based on the laboratory's published price lists.

Fundamental components

(a) Camera raw stock (normally purchased direct from the manufacturer, not through the laboratory). Total usage estimated on a per foot basis, decided by colour or black and white, negative or reversal, 35 or 16mm.

(b) Negative (or reversal) Developing. Total quantity to be processed, at the laboratory's per foot charge for that type of material; forced development usually takes a higher rate.

(c) Rush Printing. The type and gauge of rush print (positive or reversal, 35 or 16) is decided by the camera material chosen, but the production manager must estimate the proportion of printed takes to footage shot and how much to be rush printed in colour and how much in black and white. Also whether one-light or graded colour rushes are required.

(d) Negative Cutting. This, together with sound track synchronising and make-up, is charged on the number of reels, but the unit rate differs for straight cutting, auto-opticals, A and B rolls or checkerboard. Academy printing leaders and part titles must be provided.

(e) Protective Facilities. These are an optional feature and from colour negative can take the form of separation masters, colour master positives or reversal intermediates.

(f) Printing Facilities. Sometimes a full length derivative must be made from the cut original before printing can start, for instance a blow-up CRI from a Super-16 negative or a 16mm internegative from the reversal original. Costs may have to include optical effects, and a surcharge for wet gate printing.

(g) Answer Print. It is usual to charge for the first answer print at one rate and for a second print with revised grading, if required, at a somewhat lower price.

BUDGETS FOR BASIC LABORATORY WORK

The cost of camera raw stock is indicated for each example but is not included in the total, as it is not usually a laboratory-charged item. Prices for optical work and special effects are not shown since these vary so much according to the requirements and methods followed.

A. **35mm Colour Feature Film**

(Raw Stock 120,000' 35mm colour negative £6170 $17,500)

35mm Negative Developing	100,000'	£1800	$8000
35mm Graded Colour Rush Prints	15,000'	975	4500
35mm B & W Rush Prints	45,000'	1055	3150
35mm Track Negative Developing	9,000'	105	270
35mm Track Rush Prints	9,000'	210	540
Picture Negative Cutting	10 reels	190	800
Track Synchronising and Make-up	10 reels	45	120
Academy Leaders and Part Titles		45	100
35mm Colour Answer Print	9,000'	720	3600
		£5145	$21,080
Protective Materials, if required			
35mm 3-c Separation Masters	9,000'	£2565	$4320
OR 35mm Colour Master Positive	9,000'	£2025	$4050

B. **Full-length Colour Documentary by blow-up from Super-16**

(Raw Stock 40,000' 16mm colour reversal £1280 $2750)

16mm Reversal Processing	40,000'	£800	$3200
16mm Colour Reversal Rush Prints	5,000'	440	1000
16mm B & W Reversal Rush Prints	15,000'	540	1200
Picture Master Cutting, A & B, checker-board	8 reels	320	1200
A & B Black Spacing		40	100
Leaders		10	40
35mm Blow-up Internegative, A & B printed	7,200'	2880	5180
35mm one-light print from internegative	7,200'	325	1440
35mm Track Negative Developing	7,200'	85	220
Track Synchronising and Make-up	8 reels	35	100
35mm Colour Answer Print	7,200'	575	2880
		£6050	$16560

C. **35mm Colour single-reel Short**

(Raw Stock 10,000' 35mm colour negative £605 $1500)

35mm Negative Developing	10,000'	£180	$800
35mm Graded Colour Rush Prints	3,000'	195	900
35mm Track Negative Developing	800'	10	25
Picture Negative Cutting	1 reel	20	80
Track Synchronising and Make-up	1 reel	5	15
Academy Leaders		5	10
35mm Colour Answer Print	800'	65	320
		£480	$2150

197

Laboratory Charges & Budgeting (3)

Specal effects

Special effects, if required, will carry an additional charge based partly on the complexity of the work and partly on the footage of the various components involved. Fades are the simplest and therefore the cheapest, dissolves and wipes somewhat more expensive, while elaborate montage sequences and travelling matte effects may have to be the subject of specially estimated charges. Colour interpositives and dupes are charged on the length required. There are usually additional charges for printing from A and B rolls and for wet gate printing. Because the footage in optical effects is sometimes very small in comparison with the labour involved, they are often subject to a minimum charge, irrespective of their length.

Release prints

Once the answer print from the cut reel has been approved, the ordering of further release prints is usually the financial responsibility of the distributor rather than the production organisation. For these, the laboratory will normally offer a graded price schedule in which the cost per foot reduces as the number of copies ordered together increases. Orders for 3 or 4 prints at a time may well be charged at a rate almost twice that applicable to orders of 50 or more, where more efficient bulk printing methods can be used. Prints made from cut A and B rolls will always take a surcharge to cover the additional labour of double printing. The rate per foot will also be increased where release copies are specified 'without splices' or 'no frames missing,' since the avoidance of stock joins in the print involves the use of additional positive print stock.

Optical printing, whether for 16mm reduction copies from 35mm originals, for unsqueezing from anamorphic negatives or other changes of format, is always a comparatively slow operation using complex equipment and will therefore always take a higher charge per foot. Pan-and-scan printing for television use is particularly expensive because of the complex programming involved. Because of the cost of optical printing it is always advisable to have a narrow-gauge intermediate made when large numbers of 16mm or 8mm copies are to be made from a larger original.

Television commercials

Short advertising commercials for television are also subjects where the unit footage is small in comparison with the labour involved and it is general practice to price them as units in the categories 'not exceeding 15 seconds', 'not exceeding 30 seconds', etc., rather than by their exact length, unless very large numbers of copies are required.

BUDGETS FOR BASIC LABORATORY WORK

D.   16mm Colour single-reel Short

(1) Shot on Reveral Stock (Raw Stock 4000' 16mm £125 $280)

16mm Reversal Processing	4,000'	£80	$320
16mm Colour Reversal Rush Prints	1,200'	105	240
16mm Track Negative Developing	320'	5	10
Picture Master Cutting, A & B, checkerboard	1 reel	40	150
A & B Black Spacing		5	15
Leaders		5	10
Track Synchronising and Make-up		5	10
16mm Colour Reversal Answer Print, A & B printed	320'	35	95
		£280	$850

(2) Shot on Negative Stock (Raw Stock 4000' 16mm £135 $320)

16mm Negative Developing	4,000'	£70	$320
16mm Graded Colour Rush Prints	1,200'	70	240
16mm Track Negative Developing	320'	5	10
Picture Negative Cutting, A & B, checkerboard	1 reel	40	150
A & B Black Spacing		5	15
Leaders		5	10
Track Synchronising and Make-up		5	10
16mm Colour Answer Print, A & B Printed	320'	30	80
		£230	$835

Up to the Answer Print the difference between the two methods is not large, but subsequent reversal release prints are much the more expensive.

Release Print Prices

Examples of the unit price per foot for a number of copies ordered for contact printing at the same time from the same negative :

	B & W Positive		Col. Positive		Col. Reversal	
	Pence	$	Pence	$	Pence	$
35mm, optical sound (25 copies)	1.90	.040	3.00	.078	—	—
16mm, optical sound (50 copies)	1.45	.030	2.35	.058	4.10	.120
Super-8, optical sound (200 copies)	1.00	.022	2.56	.054	—	—
Super-8, magnetic sound (200 copies)	1.50	.032	3.18	.064	—	—

In general, orders for smaller numbers will take an appreciably higher price, larger orders a somewhat lower one.

Spools, cans and cassettes for prints will be an extra charge.

Terms of Business

The work of the laboratory is strictly that of a service supplier and in its relation with the production side of the motion picture industry it is in a very unusual position. It has to carry out comparatively inexpensive operations on a material whose intrinsic value is small but which may at the same time be the sole record of extremely costly creative work, possibly almost irreplaceable. Neither the cost of the raw stock nor the charges for laboratory services can bear any relation to the unknown value of the images recorded and therefore by established custom the liabilities for defective materials or operations must be limited.

The raw stock manufacturer's responsibility is usually indicated both in his general terms of business and as a notice on the label of each can of film. The effect of these is to limit liability to the replacement of material found to be faulty or defective in manufacture and specifically to exclude all consequential loss or damage of any sort.

For the laboratory the terms of business will usually state that although all reasonable care will be taken in processing and handling the customer's material, all operations are carried out at the customer's risk and the laboratory accepts no responsibility for loss or damage whatsoever. It is therefore clearly in the producer's interest to cover the film sent for processing against all risks. Insurance must cover the original material not only during the studio production stages but, perhaps even more important, also while the negative is being cut and printed for the first time, since the material is still to a degree at risk. Re-photography to replace material damaged during processing or rush printing may be very expensive, but replacement could prove literally impossible once studio work has been completed. It is for this reason that the preparation of protective facilities is recommended at the first possible moment after cutting, and insurance costs may be reduced once these are available.

Rectifying faults

Despite all the checks and inspection given to ensure the quality of the release print supplied by the laboratory, mistakes can occur and a defective copy or one incorrectly indentified may be despatched. Most laboratories will accept the responsibility of replacing, repairing or correcting such a mistake at their own expense, provided that the fault is reported and the print returned within reasonable time, usually ten days. However, liability for consequential damage is disclaimed.

The assessment of what is a reasonable print life is difficult, since so much depends on the care with which it is handled after it leaves the laboratory. It must be noted, though, that all stock manufacturers warn their customers that the dyes forming the image in a colour print are liable to change with time and that therefore prints will not be replaced as defective for fading or other alterations of colour.

This film will be replaced if found by us to be defective in manufacture, labelling or packaging, and our liability if any in respect of or consequent upon any such defects whether in original or replacement goods, shall be limited thereto, no warranty or condition whether express or implied being given by us as regards material or workmanship or fitness of goods for any particular purpose whether such purpose be known to us or not or otherwise.

NOTICE: This product will be replaced if found defective or faulty in manufacture, labelling or packaging. Subject to this, all express or implied warranties or conditions, statutory or otherwise are excluded and responsibility will not be accepted for loss or damage, consequential or otherwise, however caused.

This product will be replaced if defective in manufacture, labelling or packaging. Except for such replacement, this product is sold without other warranty or liability, even if negligence or other fault is involved. Since all colours may change in time, no replacements will be made for changes in colour.

NOTICE: This product will be replaced if found defective or faulty in manufacture, labelling or packaging. Subject to this, all express or implied warranties or conditions, statutory or otherwise, are excluded and responsibility will not be accepted for loss or damage, consequential or otherwise, however caused. Because dyes used in colour photographic materials, like other dyes, may change in time, neither film nor prints will be replaced or otherwise warranted against any change in colour.

This product will be replaced if defective. No other liability whatsoever will be accepted and all warranties and conditions statutory express or implied are excluded.

1

LIMITATION OF LABORATORY LIABILITY
Since the intrinsic value of the Customer's film clearly exceeds and bears no relationship to laboratory charges for processing, printing, and other services, the Laboratory, in accord with general practice and custom in the Laboratory industry, assumes no responsibility for loss or damage from any cause whatsoever, including loss resulting from the negligence of laboratory employees. Notwithstanding the aforegoing, in the event of loss, damage or destruction of any such films of the Customer as the result of negligence, the Laboratory will reimburse the Customer for the cost of the raw stock and any laboratory charges incurred in connection with such film, and this responsibility shall fix the limit of laboratory liability, there being no other warranty or liability.

LIABILITY OF LABORATORY
The Company respectfully points out that as prices are never proportionate to the value of the negatives and positives entrusted to it, Customers' films are received, developed, printed and stored by the Company only at the Customer's risk, and the Company, its servants, agents and sub-contractors do not accept responsibility for any loss of or damage to such (consequential or otherwise) from any cause whatsoever. All orders and contracts are accepted on the understanding that the Company is not responsible for delay or loss arising from contingencies beyond its control such as War, Strikes, Lockouts, Fires, etc., which prevent or delay the delivery of films. Customers should, therefore, insure all films entrusted to the Company against all risks.

LIMITATION OF LIABILITY
Technicolor takes every reasonable care in the processing, treating, handling and storing of the customer's material and uses all reasonable endeavours to deal with orders promptly, but all orders are accepted subject to the condition that Technicolor shall not be liable or responsible for any loss, damage or destruction of film, video tape or magnetic material or any other property or for delay unless such loss, damage, destruction or delay result from a wilful act of Technicolor or any of its employees acting within the scope of its or their authority and employment.

LABORATORY WARRANTY
Should a print be found defective, or labelled or shipped in error, the laboratory will promptly replace or repair such defective print and/or correct an error in shipment at its expense provided the defective print is returned and written notice of such imperfection and/or the error in labelling or shipment is given to the Laboratory within ten days after its arrival at destination. But in no event shall the Laboratory be liable for any consequential damages.

The Company will replace or repair any defective print at its expense provided the defective print is returned and written notice of defect is given to the Company within TEN DAYS after its arrival at destination.

2

TERMS OF BUSINESS   (1) Stock Manufacturer's Guarantees.
(2) Laboratory Liability Statements.

In Conclusion

It will have become clear that the theme of this book is better communication: the laboratory can only do a good job if they know exactly what you require and you will be able to instruct them better if you understand something of the laboratory's way of working. Laboratories serve many varied sides of the industry—directors, cameramen, editors, sound recordists, production accountants and print managers—and their corresponding operations, which are technical and often complex, are not always clearly recognised. This book is an attempt to explain the laboratory's relation to its customers.

Further Reading

SPSE/SMPTE SYMPOSIUM:
Laboratory handling of long films. Society of Photographic Scientists and Engineers and Society of Motion Picture and Television Engineers, Santa Monica, 1971.

A collection of fifteen separate papers given in a tutorial seminar on different aspects of American laboratory technology for professional motion pictures.

CORBETT, D. J.:
Motion picture and TV Film Image Control and Processing Techniques. Focal Press, London, 1968.

A complete textbook of film processing and printing equipment and sensitometric and chemical control in laboratory operations, with emphasis on the requirements of television.

BKSTS LECTURE NOTES:
Image Quality and Control. British Kinematograph Sound and Television Society, London, 1973.

A loose-leaf volume of lecture notes covering a course on photographic theory and laboratory practice for colour and B & W film processing control work in picture and sound.

RUSSELL CAMPBELL (Ed.)
Photographic Theory for Cameramen. Zwemmer, London, Barnes, New York, 1970.

A compilation prepared in association with the London Film School dealing with basic photographic theory for colour and B & W and its application in practice by cameraman and laboratory.

FIELDING, RAYMOND
Technique of Special Effects Cinematography. Focal Press, London, 1970.

A full and thorough-going treatment of all forms of this work in professional motion pictures, now extended into the field of television, from the operations of the studio Special Effects Department to those of the optical printer specialists.

Glossary

A and B Cutting (106–110) (142) (148) A method of assembling original material in two separate rolls, allowing optical effects to be made by double printing (A and B Printing).

A or B Wind (26) The two forms of winding used for rolls of film perforated on one edge only.

AR (24) Aspect ratio, the proportion of picture width to height.

ASA (40) Exposure Index or Speed Rating to denote film sensitivity, defined by the American National Standards Institution (formerly the American Standards Association).

Additive Colour (46) Colour mixture by the addition of light of the three primaries, red, green and blue.

Advance (128) The separation between a point on the sound track of a film and the corresponding picture image.

Anamorphic (24) (164) (168) (170) An optical system having different magnifications in the horizontal and vertical dimensions of the image.

Answer Print (12) (158) (160) The first print combining picture and sound submitted by the laboratory for the customers' approval.

Auto-optical (146) A method of printing dissolve effects from a single roll of negative on an automatic optical printer.

Backing (38) A black coating applied to the film base to reduce halation.

Base (16) The transparent support on which the photographic emulsion of a film is coated.

Bloop (130) A triangular patch or punched hole used to avoid the noise ofa splice in an optical sound track.

Blow-up (164–168) Enlargement of a film image.

Break-down (10) (68) The separation of a roll of camera original negative into its individual scenes.

Camera Log (64–66) A record sheet giving details of the scenes photographed on a roll of original negative.

CC Filters (46) Colour compensating filters made in precise density values of the primary and secondary colours (red, green, blue, cyan, magenta, yellow).

Cell Side (16) The base ('Celluloid') surface of a strip of film.

Change-over Cue (136) A mark at the end of a release print reel to indicate the moment at which to switch over to the next reel on the second projector.

Checker-board Cutting (144) A method of assembling alternate scenes of negative in A and B rolls allowing prints to be made without visible splices.

Cinemascope (24) (164) (168) Trade name of a system of anamorphic widescreen presentation.

Cinex Strip (70) A short test print in which each frame has been printed at a different exposure level.

Combined Print (12) See **Married Print.**

Composite Print (160) See **Married Print.**

Condensing (84) Winding a number of separate short lengths of film in one roll without joining for storage.

Continuous Printing (42–44) A method of printing in which both the original and the raw stock move continuously past the point of exposure.

Core (56) (60) A plastic cylinder on which film is wound for transport and storage.

Coupler (32) A chemical incorporated in the emulsion of colour film stocks which produces a dye image associated with the developed silver image.

Counter (56) A device for measuring lengths of film by counting the number of frames.

CP Filters (46) Colour Printing filters made in precise density values of the colours yellow, cyan and magenta.

CRI (104) Colour Reversal Intermediate, a duplicate colour negative prepared by reversal processing.

Cross Mod (124) A test method for determining the optimum print requirements for a variable area sound track.

Cue Mark (136) See **Change-over** and **Motor Cue.**

Cue sheet (106) An instruction sheet giving details of the printing for a particular roll of film.

Cutting (140–144) The selection and assembly of the various scenes or sequences of a reel of film.

Cyan (32) Blue-green colour, the complementary of red.

Dailies (Daily Rush Prints) (10) (78–80) The first positive prints made by the laboratory from the negative photographed on the previous day.

Density (76) A factor which indicates the light-stopping power of a photographic image.

Developing (28–34) The chemical process which converts a photographic exposure into a visible image.

Dissolve (88) (94–108) A transition between two scenes where the first merges imperceptibly into the second (Lap Dissolve : Mix).

Dubbing (118) The combination of several sound components into a single recording.

Dupe (104) A copy negative, short for duplicate negative.

Edit Sync (Level Sync) (Even Sync) (128) The relation between the picture and sound records during editing, when they are in alignment and not offset as for projection.

Edge Numbers (22) Coded numbers printed along the edge of a strip of film for identification.

Emulsion (16) The gelatine layer of photo-sensitive material in which the image is formed.

Fade (88) (94–108) An optical effect in which the image of a scene is gradually replaced by a uniform dark area, or vice versa.

Filter (46) A transparent material having the ability to absorb certain wavelengths of light and transmit others.

Filter Pack (46) A group of several filters, both colour and neutral density, used to correct the printer light for a particular negative.

Fixing (28–34) The removal of unexposed silver halides from the film during processing.

Flicker (78) The alternation of light and dark periods which can be visually appreciated.

Float (78) Periodic vertical movement of the image as a result of mechanical faults in camera, printer or projector.

Flop-over (90) An optical effect in which the picture is shown reversed from right to left.

Flutter (78) In sound, rapid period variation of frequency caused by unsteadiness of the film or tape drive.

Fog Level (76) The minimum density of the unexposed area of a processed film.

Footage Number (22) See **Edge Number.**

Format (24) (164) The size or aspect ratio of a motion picture frame.

Frame (24) The individual picture image on a strip of motion picture film.

Freeze Frame (90) (94) An optical printing effect in which a single frame image is repeated so as to appear stationary when projected.

Front End (8) General terms for all production and preparation work up to the Answer Print stage before Release Printing.

Gate (48) The aperture assembly at which the film is exposed in a camera, printer or projector.

Grading (70–72) (154–58) The process of selecting the printing values for colour and density of successive scenes in a complete film to produce the desired visual effects.

Hold Frame (90) (94) See **Freeze Frame.**

Hold Take (10) (66) The negative of a scene to be held for possible future use, although not chosen for rush printing.

Horse (56) A support for one or more rolls of film used on a cutting table.

Incoming Scene (88) The second scene to appear in a dissolve or wipe effect.

Inter-dupe (104) A colour duplicate negative printed from a master positive.

Intermediates (104) General term for colour masters and dupes.

Inter-positive (104) A colour master positive print.

Iris Wipe (88) A wipe effect in the form of an expanding or diminishing circle.

K (160) Kelvin, the unit of measurement used for absolute temperature and colour temperature.

Stock (16) General term for motion picture film, particularly before exposure ('raw stock').

Stock Numbers (22) Edge numbers provided on the raw stock by the manufacturer.

Stop Frame (90) (94) An optical printing effect in which a single frame image is repeated to appear stationary when projected. Also, camera exposure made one frame at a time rather than by continuous running.

Stretch Frame (90) An optical effect in which frames are regularly repeated to give the appearance of slower action.

Strip (20) Part of a wide roll of manufactured film slit to its final width for motion picture use.

Stripe (54) (176) A narrow band of magnetic coating or developing solution applied to a length of motion picture film.

Subtractive Colour (46) The formation of colours by the removal of selected portions of the white light spectrum by transparent filters or dye images.

Synchroniser (56) (140) Equipment used in editing to keep two or more strips of film exactly in step by passing them over inter-locked sprockets.

Synchronising (128) The operation of bringing the picture and sound records into their correct relation for reproduction.

Timing (70–72) (154–156) See **Grading.**

Trailer (162) A short publicity film advertising a forthcoming presentation. Also, the length of identification and protective film at the end of a reel of release print.

Travelling Matte (92) A process shot in which foreground action is superimposed on a separately photographed background by optical printing.

Trims (12) (140) Portions of a scene left over after the selected section has been used in final cutting.

Unsqueezed Print (164) (170) A print in which the distorted image of an anamorphic negative has been corrected for normal projection.

Weave (78) Periodic sideways movement of the image as a result of mechanical faults in camera, printer or projector.

Wet Printing (50) A system of printing in which the original is temporarily coated with a layer of liquid at the moment of exposure to reduce the effect of surface faults.

Widescreen (24) General term for form of film presentation in which the picture shown has an aspect ratio greater than 1·33:1.

Wipe (88) (110) Optical transition effect in which one image is replaced by another at a boundary edge moving in a selected pattern across the frame.

Zero-cut (146) A method of printing from A and B checkerboard rolls to eliminate the appearance of joins between scenes in the original.

Zoom (90) An optical effect in which the image rapidly grows larger or smaller, as though the camera moved towards or away from the object.